Stop Drug and Alcohol Addiction: A Guide for Clinical Hypnotherapists

A 6-Step Program on How to Help
Clients Overcome Drug Addiction and
Alcoholism - Fast - Through Hypnotherapy

Also by Tracie O'Keefe:

Inspiration for Survive and Prosper: Personal Transformation Out of Crisis, Vivid Publishing, 2014

Walking the Path of Wellness and Kindness
(in *Plant Powered Women*, edited by Kathy Divine), CreateSpace, 2014

Overcoming Depression and Female Learned Helplessness Through Hypnotherapy
(in *Women and Depression*), Cambridge Scholars Publishing, 2010

Trans People in Love (with Katrina Fox), Routledge, 2008

Finding the Real Me: True Tales of Sex and Gender Diversity (with Katrina Fox), Jossey Bass, 2003

Self-Hypnosis for Life: Mind, Body & Spiritual Excellence, Extraordinary People Press, 2000

Sex, Gender & Sexuality: 21st Century Transformations, Extraordinary People Press, 1999

Investigating Stage Hypnosis, Extraordinary People Press, 1998

Trans-X-U-All: The Naked Difference (with Katrina Fox), Extraordinary People Press, 1997

Stop Drug and Alcohol Addiction: A Guide for Clinical Hypnotherapists

A 6-Step Program on How to Help Clients Overcome Drug Addiction and Alcoholism - Fast - Through Hypnotherapy

Tracie O'Keefe

All proficient hypnotherapists spend thousands of hours studying, practising, reviewing, and updating their knowledge and skills to serve the customer.

Is this what our clients deserve?

FIRST EDITION, 2018

Copyright ©2018, Tracie O'Keefe

Published by Australian Health & Education Centre
An imprint of O'Keefe & Fox Industries Pty Ltd
Suite 207, 410 Elizabeth Street, Surry Hills, NSW 2010, Australia
Website: www.healtheducationcentre.com

International wholesale enquiries through Ingram.

Editing: Anita Saunders and Katrina Fox
Cover design by Ilian Georgiev
Text layout: Kassandra Bowers: www.lakazdi.com

ISBN: 978-0-9875109-1-4

Table of Contents

Acknowledgements

One of the most important parts of a therapist's journey is to honour and thank those who filled their heads with knowledge, skills and a spirit of healing. For me it was Ray Keedy-Lilly, Michael Joseph, Milton Erickson, Caroline Miller and Richard Neves, among many others too numerous to name. We learn so much from others, even by just being in their shadow.

I would also like to thank all my supervisors who have helped shaped me as a therapist over the years and provoked me into extending the limits of my clinical expertise and expectations. Particular thanks to Pamela Gawler-Wright, Nadia Hjij, Stephen Clarke, Roxene Cossill, Matthew Kalitowski, Josephine Lyon, Marcus Rigby and Alexandra Pope.

Qualifying as a therapist is only the beginning of our professional life, as our success is only ever measured by our commitment to practising and willingness to become someone else as we grow.

I would like to thank those who have invited me to speak and teach over the years, including Bruni Brewin, Mailin Colman and Lydia Deukmedjian from the Australian Hypnotherapists Association; and Lyndall Briggs from the Australian Society of Clinical Hypnotherapists.

I'm also grateful for the time I spent with Anne Peacock's lovely Pimlico hypnotherapy group and the James Braid Society in London, and my respected colleague Leon Cowen from the Academy of Applied Hypnosis in New South Wales, Australia, for our always lively dialogue on how to take hypnotherapy forward as a profession.

To all my students for going out into the world and changing it through their therapy skills, I salute you. It has been and continues to be a privilege to share this journey with you.

A special thank you to my devoted, lovely wife of 25 years, Katrina Fox, who has supported me putting this book on addiction recovery together to pass on my skills and knowledge. She is the consummate translator and editor of my ramblings and thought bubbles into comprehensible dialogue. Thank you for all the years you have supported me in private practice and teaching, even when I ignore you while I am studying and doing research.

Thank you to Simon Shaw, the biochemist who checked my science and drug listings, because without accuracy, as scientists, we are running in the dark with a bag over our heads. Thanks to my final copy editor Anita Saunders for finding the English in my Spinglish.

Finally, thank you to all my clients who have placed their trust in me to guide them out of the terrible torment of addiction to drugs and alcohol to go on to live a freer life. You may never read this because you are too busy carrying on with your lives and I honour you for your journey and accomplishment of learning to live a better life. What I learnt from you helps other people have better lives too, so your actions of bravery multiply tenfold into the world.

Preface

Millions of people die throughout the world every year as a direct result of damage caused by an addiction to drugs and/or alcohol. Even more people suffer the long-term physical and mental health damage, reduced quality of life, social isolation and homelessness caused by the abuse of drugs and alcohol. It is one of our greatest health and social problems throughout the world today. The cost of our health system runs into the trillions of dollars every year.

I have seen many people come into my practice in various states of physical distress from addiction and post-addiction, including liver failure, kidney damage, brain damage, loss of mental focus, adrenal exhaustion, vascular collapse and long-term infection, including HIV and hepatitis B and C complications, to name a few.

Mentally addicts can develop high anxiety, panic attacks, depression, paranoia, schizoid-like personality fragmentation, reclusiveness, agoraphobia, and collapse of their abilities to interact with other people in healthy and wholesome ways. They can become unemployable, isolated and rejected by their families, get into trouble with the law and often end up in prison. While they are besotted by the substance they abuse, few in retrospect would have sacrificed the quality of their lives had they known what they would lose as a result of their addiction and how things would turn out for them. By the time the addiction had taken hold, however, they felt they no longer had a choice or the ability to stop using that substance.

Addiction is a medical emergency. It is a time when a person has lost control of their physical body and mental ability to maintain homeostasis, so the body deviates into sickness and disease. That person needs help and empathy. They may not want help or believe they have an addiction, sometimes for decades, and labour under the delusion they are in control of their lives, but they are not. Some come to the realisation they need help and some do not.

Simply giving someone with an alcohol or drug addiction more drugs of a different kind is not helping them get over their addiction; it is a substituted addiction of perhaps a more socially acceptable kind that does not profit the patient. It does, however, create big profits for pharmaceutical companies which may indeed, in the case of prescription drugs, have been contributors to the problems in the first place.

I have spent my entire life surrounded by addiction. My father was a drunk with mental health issues, violent, abusive and psychopathic. On pay day, during the few times he worked, he could not pass the pub on the way home without spending a great deal of his wages, leaving his family hungry and poor. In my early teenage years I was a child who was forcibly given LSD as part of a medical experiment.

At college when I was 15, I was surrounded by people experimenting with LSD, magic mushrooms and cannabis. The 1970s was a period of youth cultural revolution when young people wanted to challenge the old social order in the UK and students were caught up in the psychedelic movement. In the co-counselling group I started at college, we found that drug abuse was often a problem but it was too dangerous to disclose to the college for fear of sanction. Even the boy I lived with and was in love with when I was 15 and 16 died from a drug overdose.

When I was a dancer and singer in my youth in London and abroad in the theatre, I was surrounded by artists taking cocaine, amphetamines, opium and heroin, and smoking marijuana.

Some of those who developed addictions died young but some of them who lived can often no longer remember those years and have aged poorly.

Like many young people, I experimented with various drugs and alcohol, none of which had any long-term appeal. For many decades I have lived a highly rewarding life, clean and sober, which has allowed me to be in a very strong position to help those who suffer addiction. My life has not been conventional, whatever that may be, so I probably fit into the straight edge movement of alternative people who live clean and sober lives.

In the therapy room, the people who come to see me for help with addiction hail from a much wider sector of society, including accountants, lawyers, judges, royalty, anaesthesiologists, psychiatrists, stockbrokers, police and military personnel, politicians, clergy, train drivers, carpenters, homemakers and many others. Indeed, there is no sector of society that addiction does not affect. Given certain conditions, any one of us could succumb to substance abuse, at any time of our lives.

The human body is a biomechanical, biochemical machine with millions of years of evolution behind its development. As a clinical naturopath, I see it as a thing of exquisite beauty and sophistication. Given the right circumstances, it generally has the innate ability to self-repair and correct its functions when something goes wrong. If you take that ability away from someone or subdue it by drugging them, they often cannot find their way to health and healing.

Naturopaths use the phrase 'clean living' to describe the way of living that is closest to nature. It involves eating high-quality foods, not taking unnecessary drugs, low exposure to toxins, exercising regularly and living a low-stress life with good social relationships. We talk about having clean blood and organs, meaning they are without infection and disorder. People come to me to learn how to live clean, healthy and long lives.

As a clinical hypnotherapist, psychotherapist and counsellor, I see the human mind as a continuous series of opportunities to create self-fulfilment, enjoy life's experiences and interact with the rest of the world in a sustainable, rewarding way. I am in awe of the capacity of human cognition, achievement and ability for compassion, and as a therapist, that is always at the centre of my clinical philosophy.

During addiction, the mind plays tricks on itself, deluding the individual that they are safe and not in danger as a direct result of the actions of taking drugs or alcohol. People will take themselves to the brink of death and beyond in a quest to experience one more time with the substance, devoid of all reason and logic. For them, the trance of being an addict seems unbreakable.

I, like many clinicians, have observed that of the thousands of clients I have worked with, there are common factors that help them recover from addiction. Clinical hypnotherapy and psychotherapy can help them develop their personalities to become a different kind of person and live clean and sober, as I shall show you in these pages.

The 6-Step Stop Drugs and Alcohol Clinical Hypnotherapy Model that I have developed over the years and teach to hypnotherapists is a clean and sober model. The whole premise of my methods is that they work fast. It is a substance elimination model, since it is the substance that has caused the addiction in the first place. For thousands of people this has improved their life beyond measure, allowing them to live a life fully recovered from active addiction.

To be a therapist who helps clients recover from drug and alcohol addictions is a deeply fulfilling experience for me. When I teach hypnotherapy masterclasses I know that those therapists will be more skilled to be part of changing people's lives forever by helping them gain relief from the addiction.

How to use this book
This book is written as a teaching tool to help you systemise your approach as a clinical hypnotherapist with clients who are seeking

to recover from drug and alcohol addiction. It is written solely for those trained in hypnotherapy or who are studying hypnotherapy. I work systematically in my practice. Although I may employ many different hypnotherapeutic philosophies, disciplines and techniques with a client, I employ structure in my work. Since I have worked with so many people to help them recover from addiction, I discovered not only does the therapist need a structure in therapy but so does the client, which allows us to achieve around a 90% success rate.

You will learn the six steps in the recovery program I teach you. Each step is broken down further to help you understand the mechanics of the techniques I use. They are the six steps that an addict must go through progressively to attain a complete recovery. If a step is missed out, the chance of a relapse becomes high.

When reading and practising the techniques, take time to familiarise yourself with the reasons I use each step and the sequences of those steps. Constantly observe and listen to the clients you are working with as you collect feedback about how the process works. You will have your successes and you will have your failures as you become more proficient and adept at helping alcoholics and addicts overcome their addictions. As with all learning and study, repetition, practice and adaptability is the road to success.

References

The references are organised chapter by chapter. Any single source of referencing is unreliable, including research, which is frequently biased and outdated. This is also the case for academia, the media, the internet and patients themselves. For greater balance of information, I have used a broad spectrum of sources. They are provided for your own further education to allow you to broaden your knowledge of alcohol and drug addiction and recovery.

Scripts

Scripts are used in hypnotherapy to guide hypnotherapists but they are not to be used verbatim for hypnotherapy itself because every client and session is different. I present them with bold type indications for important verbal marking where certain suggestions need more emphasis. The scripts I include offer you some of the pragmatics, semantics, psycholinguistics and hypnotic language patterns I have used for those clients. In the brackets, I have included comments on what hypnotic techniques I am aiming for and my thoughts behind the process of change I am inciting in the client.

Some of my students find it easier to highlight the parts of the script that the therapist actually speaks when practising verbal delivery, particularly if you have any form of dyslexia.

Each hypnotherapist uses their own particular and different language patterns. Continuous verbatim monologues do not allow clients to digest or process any unconscious changes as they process information. In the teaching scripts '…' denotes time for rest, breathing and processing. It is almost a linguistic lyrical approach.

The scripts also include conversational hypnotic interchange between me and the client which guides and provokes them towards the psychotherapeutic change I am seeking, both consciously and unconsciously. All of this is hypnotic, whether it is conscious conversation or somnambulistic.

Addressing the point about using the phrase 'clean and sober'

I am aware that some people and academics want to abandon the phrase 'clean and sober' because they associate the word 'clean' with implications of social stigma around addicts being 'dirty' people. Let us remember, however, that linguistically the phrase 'clean and sober' is in common usage with recovered addicts. It is a powerful phrase for many who carry pride and achievement in their identity as being clean, sober and free from addiction. It is, for them, a badge of honour. Hypnotically it is a strong, decisive, effective and direct command suggestion. From a naturopathic point of view, it denotes a life with minimal toxins. We give language its pragmatic value and political correctness by the way we use it, not by the way others want us to use it. In my work with clients, the terminology is used in a positive, reinforcing way.

IMPORTANT NOTE: Please note that with the trance scripts, conventions for grammar and punctuation have been ignored. This is a deliberate strategy to demonstrate the flow of commands and depotentiation of conscious resistance by implementing cognitive overload, which happens with lack of pauses in communication.

I also include for your convenience a glossary at the back of the book so you can find a quick reference for words or techniques you may not yet understand.

Each hypnotherapist evolves their own way of working with people. I hope you enjoy learning some ways I work with clients to help them recover from addiction.

Every hour of every day thousands of people throughout the world are recovering from addiction to recreational drugs, prescription medication and alcohol, and I hope this book helps you to help even more people.

1 Drugs in a Global Society

Shamanic practices around drugs and alcohol

The use of drugs and alcohol in shamanic practices has been a global, time-honoured tradition and little understood by Western academia or society. The word 'drug' is derived from the French word 'drogue', meaning supply stock or provision, referring to dried plants, spices or herbs that have been used by apothecaries. In less-developed cultures these were collected by shamans.

Potterton (1983) shows us how Culpeper used plants from an apothecary perspective in the 1600s for healing purposes. When we look back thousands of years at cave paintings we can see shamans using plants to induce altered states of awareness for healing practices, festivals, rites of passage, fertility worship and celebrations. McKenna (1992) opines that this is a different use of plants from apothecaries because the substance is specifically used to create altered states of awareness, such as psychedelic or hallucinatory experiences.

From an anthropological and philosophical point of view, we can see that those experiences do not fit into the Western medical model, as proposed by, for example, the American Psychiatric Association (2013), as that model is bourgeois, where the doctor is the authority and the patients largely submissive. What we have to be careful of when we look at the use of mind-altering substances in cultures is that we do not see this solely as substance abuse, because it can be ceremonial and not generally a day-to-day occurrence. In shamanic experiences the patient is guided on their own exploration by the shaman. It is important to note that this is a different kind of drug use from drug abuse seen in Westernised societies.

Harrelson (1969) shows us that early pagan matriarchal cultures used menstrual blood, probably mixed with alcohol, to induce altered states of awareness during fertility festivals. Pagan cultures fermented vegetables, grain and fruits to produce alcoholic beverages to mark their ceremonies. The Christian church uses wine to celebrate Holy Communion and represent the blood of Christ. Menstrual blood was also seen as strength to defeat the enemy. Alcohol was also used to celebrate intertribal battles in war-like and invading cultures.

Belief systems change from country to country and region to region, as does the use of different mind-altering plant sources. Kilham (2014) describes how in South America, native cultures use herbs such as ayahuasca, under the guidance of a tribal shaman. The person is under a hallucinogenic influence which is supposed to transport them into other worlds on a spiritual quest. The trip can last up to a week and members of the tribe stay with the person to look after them during their internal journey, sometimes guided by the shaman.

Carlos from South America came to see me as he had suffered severely from Crohn's Disease. He went into the jungle in South America with a shaman and took ayahuasca. He was hallucinating for a week and reportedly weak for several weeks afterward. He explained, however, that it was a life-changing experience for him where he came to terms with his diagnosis and was able to cope with the treatments he needed far better and with less stress. When I saw him 18 months later he had never used ayahuasca again.

Endredy (2015) reports that peyote, a psychedelic substance from a cactus, is used by Native American cultures which is part of the culture of native Mexicans. Taking it is part of their journey to discover the spiritual world and explore who they are as a person. It is called 'humble learning'. The experience varies from tribe to tribe, region to region and language to language. In some cultures the person connects with their animal guides and ancestors for guidance and in others the experience is more about personal transformation. These experiences are profoundly influenced by rituals and non-Western belief systems that have a close association with the land and nature.

> *I met Napewastewin in the 1990s. She was from the Native American Sioux tribe and a psychotherapist. We met at a medical conference in Bavaria, Germany, and she explained how she took peyote and walked on the land to speak to her spirit guides. I remember we stopped at a poster written by some geneticists who proposed that a particular gene was responsible for a particular behaviour. In the garden having tea afterwards, I asked what she thought of that presentation and her reply was: "I never trusted people in white coats." As it happens, when the mapping of the human genome was completed, she was proved to be right and the scientists were wrong but there was great wisdom in her considerations given that spirituality in her culture was valued over science.*

Stamets (1996) says magic mushrooms (psilocybin) have been used since human culture began. There are ancient cave murals and rock paintings in Algeria that go back to prehistoric times depicting humans' use of hallucinogens. Since mushrooms will grow virtually anywhere, there are many different kinds of mushrooms with varying strengths of hallucinogenic effects. While they are used in divinatory and spiritual ceremonies, they are also used in personal exploration and transformational experiences. Letcher (2008) suggests this usage traditionally belonged to shamanic practices that have also been used by artists and intellectuals throughout time for inspirational and creative thinking.

Sharna, 32, came to see me for help with confidence when she was starting a business making face creams from natural substances. She already had a clothing line that sold very well at music festivals. Her parents had been pagans and festival organisers who took magic mushrooms, and she did too until she was 25 when she gave birth to her son. Many of her clothing and material designs were inspired by her hallucinogenic journeys on magic mushrooms. She had taken magic mushrooms in excess of 50 to 60 times and had no adverse effects. She had never drunk alcohol, smoked or used any other drugs.

According to Maragh, Howell, & McPherson (2001), Leonard Howell set up a Rastafarian community called the 'Pinnacle' where they grew and smoked marijuana. Future generations adopted the biblical interpretation of a Rastafarian's rights to smoke weed daily as a sacrament. In Jamaica Rastafarians smoke marijuana sometimes every day. For some it is seen as part of their religious practice which is a hybrid between the Old Testament and some of the New Testament. It is very much a male-oriented community, with men sometimes seen as having the right to father many children with different women.

I (the author) remember back in London in the 1970s living a few doors away from where Bob Marley, the Rastafarian singer and musician, was staying in Chelsea. The summer was hot with a light breeze that continually blew the smell of weed out of his apartment. Of course it was illegal to possess and imbibe marijuana, but the British imperial white government did not want in any way to be seen arresting such a popular religious black man at the height of his fame. A court case around religious freedom is something the British Crown Prosecution Service knew they were unlikely to win.

Long & Mongan (2014) say that 75% of alcohol consumption in Ireland is due to binge drinking. Celtic cultures such as the

Irish celebrate a person's life after their funeral by holding a wake where there are liberal amounts of alcohol and people are excused if they get drunk and make fools of themselves as they tell long stories about the deceased. Ireland is a country where alcohol flows freely to mark many occasions.

Paul, a 24-year-old Irishman, came to see me to stop smoking. He was a regular at an Irish pub in Sydney. Going to the Irish pub was a chance for him to catch up with other Irish people after work, so he went most nights a week. It was an unwritten social code that the men would drink at least four or five long glasses of beer and some whiskies every night to be sociable. When he did some calculations, he found he spent more money on alcohol than he did on his rent. He did not think he had a major problem with alcohol, nor did the people he mixed with who did the same.

There are a wide range of substances used from nature to induce altered states of awareness and I cannot touch on all of them in this book due to space. There are many concoctions, mixtures and blends that are not artificially manufactured drugs and originate from transformational and mind-exploring experiences in specific cultures. What we need to bear in mind when we consider those experiences as hypnotists is that the altered states of awareness begin before imbibing the substance. The trance of expectation and imaginary experience begins at the very first thought of taking those substances and is shaped by the cultural experiences before, during and after the intoxication.

Reynar (2008) reminds us that the production and use of alcohol in modern societies has a history that continues from ancient times when monks produced alcoholic drinks to make a living for a thousand years. Gately (2002) states the introduction of tobacco into Europe in the 15th century started the long-term intoxication through smoking that spread throughout the globe over the past 400 years. Booth (1999) explores the introduction of opium dens into Europe and America which were brought from the orient due to exploration and trading. Rasmussen (2011) researched the wide use of amphetamines within military personnel from all sides in the Second World War to increase battle performance.

As therapists it is paramount that we understand the world in which our patients live, even though we cannot follow them around with a magnifying glass. We need to understand the socio-political context that creates the environment in which addictions exist and thrive. Only by understanding social contexts can we understand the addictive trances that our clients are living inside their minds and performing in their lives.

Perhaps you have never had contact with drug or alcohol users or abusers, or you may have some training in addiction recovery. If you appear naive to clients coming to see you for cessation of addiction, the client will not appreciate your skills as a clinical hypnotherapist and clinician. For me professionally as a therapist, studying medical sociology has greatly increased my ability to understand my clients' worldview, their circumstances and what a diagnosis means to them, and increased my clinical success with addiction cessation.

I see the thousands of people I have worked with who suffered addictions to drugs and alcohol as much a product of their environmental influences and circumstances as well as being biochemically, physiologically, behaviourally and cognitively dysfunctional. The patient never exists in isolation to their environment, so to help these people stop the addictions, we are wise to also treat them in relation to the world in which they live.

Examination of Egyptian remains has revealed that there was widespread use of cocaine in those times. Scholarly texts of ancient Rome show that the use of alcohol became a public order issue at times. Drug use in ancient American culture extended beyond using psychotropic mushrooms, to licking toad skins that produced secretions which induced hallucinations.

The addiction to drugs and alcohol is a worldwide problem, always has been, and always will be. Indeed, the 2013 United Nations Office on Drugs and Crime (2012) *World Drug Report* states that substance abuse affects 27 million people.

Even in cultures where there are prohibitions on drugs and alcohol, there are still those individuals today who are secretly involved in substance abuse. Okrent (2011) examined how the North American prohibition on alcohol in the 1930s produced a whole industry of speakeasies where illegal alcohol was sold. Chalabi (2016) strongly contests that the global strategies of criminalising drug use have proved effective in stopping people experimenting with drugs and helping substance abusers overcome their addictions. This becomes more evident when we consider that the use of the term 'substance abuse' is wide and includes alcohol and prescription drugs that are obtained both legally and illegally, not just illegal drugs such as cocaine, amphetamines or opioids.

In countries such as Saudi Arabia where there is a complete ban on alcohol because it is a Muslim country that complies to the strict teachings of the Quran, people brew alcohol at home and there is a level of alcohol use and abuse (Cacciottolo, 2015). T. W (2015) of *The Economist* reviewed how dealers still supply addicts in countries where dealing drugs is punishable by death.

The US has one of the largest prison populations per capita in the world. The US Department of Justice, Bureau of Justice Statistics (2016) states that in 2015 nearly half of federal prisoners incarcerated on September 30, 2015 had been sentenced for drug offences. The increasing convictions for drug use means America is continually having to build more prisons. Those crimes include public order offences, possession, dealing drugs, burglary, robbery for money for drugs, and drug-induced violent crimes such as assault, rape and murder. Since America has openly been involved in a war on illegal drug use for over a hundred years, it is clear the strategy is not working.

In contrast, other countries, such as the Netherlands (Government of the Netherlands, 2017), state they are tackling their addiction problems differently. In Holland, for example, drug use has been divided into soft drugs and hard drugs: soft drugs being alcohol and cannabis, and harder drugs being amphetamines and opioids. The laws that could punish soft drug use are not generally enforced (5g of marijuana for personal use or the cultivation of five plants), unless it involves large-scale production and dealing. Illegally importing or exporting drugs is still considered a serious offence.

Whilst Holland is still one of the world's major manufacturers and distributors of illegal recreational drugs, which is punishable by long terms of imprisonment, it sees personal drug abuse problems as being a public health issue rather than a justice issue. Boztas (2016) reports in *The Telegraph* that the responsibility for Dutch policy on public drug addiction seems to lie between the Heath Department and Justice Department. Holland has a strong social public medicine system, as opposed to America, which is essentially a private medicine system. Consequently, the Netherlands now has much lower drug convictions and it is currently having to close prisons for lack of prisoners to put in them (Boztas, 2016).

Ingraham (2015) looks at the Portugal model that decriminalised drug use in 2001 yet still has strict laws for dealing, manufacturing and transporting drugs. Whilst getting caught with small amounts of drugs is still illegal, the person gets a small fine, not a criminal record or imprisonment, and may be referred to a treatment program. Deaths from drug overdoses in Portugal are now reportedly down to almost zero.

Ingraham (2015) also looked at how Portugal took the money it used to spend on severely penalising and incarcerating drug offenders and put that money into rehabilitation programs. Drug abuse in Portugal has fallen dramatically, along with a decline in drug-related HIV and hepatitis C infections. There is also a correlation to the decline in the use of alternative drug sources, which may not be illegal drugs but are substances often used by people seeking highs, such as synthetic marijuana and bath salts. Dennis (2015) reviewed how, when we look at social issues around addiction, it is important for us to look at the cultures that encourage prescription addiction as a way of life. Nearly 60% of Americans are taking prescription medication. America has the highest use of anti-depressants in the world. This only calculates the official medications and does not include medications such as Ritalin and opioid painkillers that are then sold onto the street by drug dealers. Breggin (2013), an American psychiatrist, exposes how, once patients are started on psychiatric medications, medical professionals are reluctant to withdraw them from that medication for fear they may be sued.

America is currently the biggest world economy, with China catching up, so it has the most money to spend. Since America is mainly a private medical system built on profit, the prescribing of drugs becomes an enormous revenue stream for doctors. A report on *BBC News* (Anderson, 2014) stated that pharmaceutical companies' profits in 2013 outstripped banks, insurance, oil and gas, and media. Pfizer alone made a 42% profit and many doctors have shares in those companies. So frequently those prescription medication addictions are driven by profits, not the welfare of the patient, and once the patient is hooked, they could be a revenue stream for doctors and drug companies for life.

This profit-driven approach is also condoned by the American Psychiatric Association (APA) (2013) in the publication of the APA's *Diagnostic and Statistical Manual of Mental Disorders* (DSM, 2013), the latest being the *DSM-5* edition, which is frequently used throughout the world. The quantification of a mental disorder in this manual is frequently culturally bound to the American model of medicine for profit that defines a psychopathology and then profitably medicates the patient, often to the point of addiction.

Within medicine, psychiatry, psychology, psychotherapy and sociology, many of those classifications are controversial and contested as a quest to create illness and sell pharmaceuticals.

The Food and Drug Administration (FDA) in the US states in the 'Frequently Asked Questions about the FDA Drug Approval Process' (US Department of Health and Human Services, Food and Drug Administration, n.d.) on its website that for a drug company to get its drug passed as a prescription drug by the FDA, it must provide studies that show benefits for using the drug. In reality a company may carry out hundreds of studies that show no benefit and even demonstrate harm, but the pharmaceutical company can hide those studies and not have to declare them, even for decades, when considerable harm has evidently been done by the drug.

Angell (2005) explains that of course from a research perspective, it is the design of the study that determines what results the study can show. A researcher can include or exclude results according to what they wish to prove. Since nearly all drug trials are funded privately by large pharmaceutical companies, it is easy to see that the company has the ability to present the results that they wish to the FDA or any other country's drug administration bodies. When a drug gains legal status and is prescribed, it can produce billions of dollars a year in profit. We can clearly see the potential danger here for marketing a drug first of all for profit and not necessarily patient management or cure.

Finkelstein (2008) lays out how the legitimacy of bodies such as the FDA authenticating medications becomes more complex when we look at how many of the board members of the FDA and other such bodies also work for the very drug companies that are trying to have their medications passed. Even those who do not work for drug companies can go on to become highly paid consultants for these companies after they leave the FDA. The high risk of conflict of interest and corruption increases dramatically when we learn that drug companies actually give funds to the FDA. So the reality of the situation is that such bodies are frequently in the pocket of the drug companies.

Blumenthal (2012) reminds us that it is also important to remember how powerful pharmaceutical drug companies are and the millions of dollars they spend every year on political lobbyists to protect their income streams. The over-prescribing of psychiatric drugs got out of hand at the end of the 1980s when drug companies were allowed to advertise their products on the television in the US and to the general public. Donahue (2006), in reviewing the history of drug advertising, shows this has led to mass over-consumption of drugs in America and throughout the world.

Tasca, Rapetti, Carta, & Fadda (2012), from a feminist perspective, looked at the damage done to women's rights by the psychoanalyst Sigmund Freud and others who propagated the idea of women's menstrual and menopause mood changes being a kind of hysteria. Halbreich, Halbreich, and Jensvold (1996) analysed that since many psychiatrists went on to be trained as psychoanalysts, they medicated women and unnecessarily removed their wombs and ovaries in an attempt to correct their supposed neurosis. Even up until the 1960s in the natural medicine world, homeopaths such as Clarke (1970) were seeing women's reproductive cycles as hysterical illnesses to be cured. This was also perpetuated by the 18th-century neurologist and hypnotist Charcot who posited that hypnosis and trance states are a form of hysteria (Owen, 1971). This fed into psychiatry in the 20th century, causing women to be over-medicated with prescribed long-term drugs for being supposedly emotionally unstable and in a hysterical trance.

The psychiatrist R.D. Laing was majorly responsible, as a prominent public figure, for pushing against psychiatry's continual pathologising and medicating of patients to the point of addiction (Boyers & Orrill, 1971). Eventually, exasperated by psychiatry, he left medicine and practised as a psychoanalyst.

The irony was, however, that he himself suffered from alcoholism and liberally used psychedelic drugs.

The psychiatrist Szasz (2008) spent much of his career criticising psychiatry for being largely a made-up science where people are often misdiagnosed with a fictitious illness and medicated when they experience psychological and social difficulties. In the documentary *Psychiatry: The Marketing of Madness: Are We All Insane?* (Citizens Commission on Human Rights, 2009), it is suggested that psychiatric medications are being used to cure unprovable illnesses and suppressing natural healing. Moore (1998) demonstrates that more people end up in hospital for complications from prescribed drugs than from automobile accidents, and furthermore, many of those are the results of addictive psychiatric medications.

Breggin (2014) heavily criticised the passing of Prozac by the FDA. In his book *Against Prozac* he showed the dubious circumstances where only certain members of the FDA board were available on a weekend to pass the drug and that trials had not supported its use as an effective anti-depressant. Many other anti-depressants have also been passed without substantial evidence of their effectiveness.

Branley & Scott (2014) showed that medical staff frequently try to play amateur psychiatrist, diagnosing patients with depression or anxiety, and medicating them to the point where they become addicted to the medication. This happens particularly with children. A major problem occurs when general practitioners continually prescribe medications to help patients overcome a life crisis. The patients often develop a dependence on the drugs, leading to addiction. These staff can often find themselves in a difficult position with medical boards if they do not medicate. They may be held up on negligence charges if they do not offer the patients medication, even after consultations lasting only 10 minutes or less.

Holland (2010) documented how in the 1930s the US authorities made the growing and using of hemp illegal. This was not due to mass public intoxication but pressure from the cotton companies which were threatened by hemp as a competitive superior fabric. Hemp was renamed marijuana to demonise its use as an intoxicating drug in the public's eyes.

Allen (2015) notes that from 1886-1929, cocaine was present in Coca-Cola in varying amounts. In those days cocaine was legal and thought of as a medicine. As censorship arrived in Hollywood in the late 1920s and early 1930s and a more American puritanical attitude emerged, cocaine was made illegal so Coca-Cola switched to using caffeine in its products.

Leary (1990), who was a key proponent of the Western recreational drug revolution, says major recreational use of drugs began in the 1960s as post-Second World War attitudes of baby boomers became more liberal and they wanted to explore beyond social norms. It was very much influenced by music and culture with the arrival of television and popular radio. Brown and Gaines (2002) report that the most famous global music group of the times was the British pop group The Beatles who had used stimulants such as Benzedrine and Preludin in the late 1950s and then went on to be publicly seen using acid and marijuana in the 1960s. The influence of their actions spread across the Western world as young people from many countries followed suit.

In America, Leary, a psychologist, writer, teacher and experimenter at Harvard University, was fired in 1963 (Greenfield, 2008). He had been involved in experiments giving undergraduate students hallucinogenic drugs including LSD (Lysergic acid) and psilocybin (magic mushrooms). He believed LSD showed potential for use in psychiatry. He was a regular user of drugs and promoted the phrase "turn on, tune in and drop out". He amassed a huge cult following, leading to the psychedelic revolution where it became trendy and popular to try drugs. Doctors, such as Grof (1980), were also involved in using LSD in psychotherapy, with Grof beginning his research in the 1960s in what was then Czechoslovakia.

Brown (2017) notes that cocaine became much more popular in the 1970s with the advent of rock stars like David Bowie who was a public regular user and, again, culture followed art. It also became more available as growing of the coca plant increased as a cash crop in South America and was smuggled to the West. Streatfeild (2002) writes how it became seen as a performance-enhancing drug and was used in sexual rituals, particularly by stockbrokers and bankers to tolerate the stress of dealing, as well as becoming a party drug.

Since opium has been used in medicine for thousands of years and been converted to morphine for pain relief, it was readily available in the West. Musto (2002) looks at heroin before it was made illegal in many countries and how it was previously marketed by the pharmaceutical company Bayer from the 1890s, including being marketed for children. It was not widely used as a recreational drug until the 1960s when it became more fashionable. Clear's (2016) interviews show how indeed the Vietnamese gave heroin to the American soldiers during the Vietnam War to get the solders addicted and incapacitated. Poppies for heroin are among the world's most lucrative cash crops, along with coffee. Whilst people who choose heroin are selective and it is not tried by many, heroin addicts become loyal customers because of the drug's perceived highly addictive nature.

Eisher (1989) considers the party drug revolution really took off at the end of the 1980s with the emergence of ecstasy (3, 4-Methylenedioxymethamphetamine [MDMA]). Created as far back as 1913, scientists were unsure what to do with it and once upon a time tested it as a truth drug. It is a drug that creates a warm, fuzzy feeling where people become extremely friendly towards each other and it induces empathy and sociability. Saunders (1997) believes its emergence was very much linked with hardcore house and techno music that lent itself well to a party atmosphere. Collin (1997) remembers that this gave birth to the rave scene where thousands of people would turn up unexpectedly at random places to have a mass makeshift party. Since it is such a social drug, ecstasy became very popular very quickly and spread throughout the world as the rave scene emerged into the club scene. What also escalated with ecstasy is that it was often cut with amphetamines, which got people hooked.

Ohler (2016) unearthed documents in Berlin that showed crystal methamphetamine (also known as meth or ice) was heavily used in the Second World War by German forces. Crystal meth is a more pure form of amphetamine than common street speed. It was used by Nazi soldiers when they marched into Paris during the Second World War, under Hitler's orders. Hitler himself was addicted to heroin, used methamphetamine and ordered all the soldiers to be administered the drug to give them endurance during the invasion. It is a drug that has been around since the early 19th century.

Bonné (2013) observed that in the 1990s meth became more popular as people began to set up meth labs in their homes or warehouses and manufactured large amounts for distribution. Brennan (2016) says it became a very popular drug in the gay male community where taking meth and having sex became fashionable to enhance sexual sensation, known as 'chemsex'. Meth is today one of the most prevalent and addictive drugs in circulation. The problem is that the addiction occurs very quickly and leads to fast physiological, emotional and cognitive decline.

As has been clearly shown, drug and alcohol use and experimentation is part of human nature physically, psychologically and socially, particularly with the young who are seeking to push the boundaries and explore their experiences. For many cultures it is purely a spiritual pursuit, often connected with the social group or tribal experience. This frequently overlaps with a person's health pursuits. People by nature form into tribes of many kinds and live the trance of that tribe as well as their individual trances. McRae (2001) posits it is the tribal beliefs system that determines whether the drugs are seen as spiritual extensions of the natural or supernatural world or whether they are seen in a scientific context.

For people in the Western developed world, taking drugs and alcohol to attain an altered state of awareness can also be a spiritual experience, despite society imposing scientific rhetoric onto those experiences. Foster (2011) says it is innate within all cultures that new generations will want to have their own experiences and create their own belief systems, heroes and generational memories. This is often under the experiences of mind-altering substances.

The prohibition or illegality of drug and alcohol experiences clearly does not stop people from experimenting with mind-altering substances. When we look at the American 'Summer of Love' in 1967 when more than 100,000 young people of the hippie generation came together in San Francisco to "turn on, tune in and drop out", we can see they were unafraid of the law. Stevens (1993) tells us that it was cultural leaders and intellectuals such as Timothy Leary, Aldous Huxley, Allen Ginsberg, Ken Kesey and Charles Manson that inspired this generation's drug taking, which turned out well for some but not for others.

Greenfield (2008) tells us Leary was continually arrested for drugs throughout the 1960s and 1970s, appeared on the CIA's and FBI's list of dangerous persons and at some stage had to move around the world to avoid re-arrest. Ultimately he became a profuse writer, counter-culture superhero and intellectual, who took drugs and published until he died.

Barry (1989) says Ginsberg was involved in drugs and alcohol at different times in his life and remained a driving intellectual force of poetry, writing for the Beat Generation. He became a campaigner for gay rights and the peaceful end to the Vietnam War, as well as being a practising Buddhist.

Huxley (Laura, 1991) discloses that her husband Aldous Huxley used hallucinogenic drugs for the last 10 years of his life to open his mind and he believed it gave him inspiration as a writer, as it had done for Lewis Carroll. She said he asked to be injected with LSD at his death. He remains one of the greatest writers of his generation.

Guinn's (2014) investigation into Manson reveals he had been a petty criminal throughout his life and had a history of mental instability, at times being admitted to a psychiatric hospital, before becoming a cult leader and descending into paranoia and psychopathy. The use of LSD for him and his followers led them to being involved in several murders and imprisoned for life.

Lehmann-Haupt (2001), in the *New York Times*, described Ken Kesey as "the Pied Piper of the psychedelic era" in regard to his prolific literary skills as Kesey went on to write the book, published in 1962, *One Flew Over the Cuckoo's Nest*. In the 1970s it was made into the popular film of the same name. An advocate of LSD and personal freedom to explore the mind, Kesey wrote about the institutionalised psychiatric abuse, forced incarceration and medication prevalent at this time.

Campos & Overton (2011) tell us when we look at the sociology of mind-altering substances such as alcohol and drugs, we can see that in traditional cultures, where that experience remains spiritual through the use of substances such as ayahuasca, there are shamanic figures to help guide people who use those substances. For whatever reasons the demonisation and prohibition of those substances in cultures wipes out those roles in that society. This leaves a void where individuals embarking on substance-induced altered states have no guides. Some who may have the intellectual capacity and a good mental state may benefit from those experiences. Others, however, who do not have the intellectual fortitude or are not mentally stable, can often get into psychological trouble during those experiences and may also become addicted to those substances.

Hames (2012) observes that alcohol use in many parts of the world is legal, driven by advertising and peer pressure to be part of the party or social event atmosphere that promotes its consumption.

The interesting thing is that intoxication is rarely remembered as a pleasant experience and a hangover is debilitating, but people can feel compelled to imbibe alcohol due to social pressure. With the industrialisation of alcohol production in the 20th century came some of the best profits on the stock market and for governments through huge, stable annual tax revenues.

One of the major perpetrators of addiction is the addiction recovery industry itself which is, according to *Forbes*, worth around $35 billion USD a year in America alone (Munro, 2015). Smith & Knezev (2012) calculate that whilst America consumes more than 50% of the drugs in the world, it amounts to only 5% of the world's population. It is a 'for profit' medical system so the addiction industry produces huge profits and is often driven by those profits, not by results. The financial worth of a client in a rehabilitation unit can be anything up to $40,000 or more per month.

McLellan (2002) evaluates that many treatments applied to addicts take too long to produce results, may produce a low level of successful results and in many cases do not produce results at all. However, since being an addict in society is not acceptable, governments continually guide people into treatments, so an addict can end up a chronic patient. They then produce a large and long-term source of income for the addiction industry, even without results. Add to that the natural lack of compliance that many patients exhibit in all branches of medicine – sometimes up to 50% – and we can see that the addiction recovery industry is not always driven by results, since an addict who does not recover can be more profitable than a patient who does.

Kelly (2015) in the *Canberra Times* reported the cutting of funding to the Australian Capital Territory's only residential addiction care unit in the midst of signs of greater demand for services. This is all too common a scenario as drug and alcohol rehabilitation is generally low on politicians' agendas as they do not see the issue as a vote winner with the public. Government-funded addiction recovery programs exist often on precarious funding. Changes of power bases within government departments, new political parties getting into power and changes in social attitudes all contribute to either the provision or withdrawal of funding for addiction projects, often without good reason. Provision of care for addicts by governments rarely ever meets demand.

O'Hara (2012) in *The Guardian* pointed out that when governments cut back funding, much of the work in addiction recovery is by default shunted onto the voluntary sector. The voluntary addiction recovery sector is a fundamental pillar of many societies that is frequently unrecognised for its level of work. The projects dealing with addicts may be run by religious organisations such as the Catholic Church, charitable foundations or, to a large part, by self-help groups such as Alcoholics Anonymous (AA) or Narcotics Anonymous (NA). Not only are they involved in addiction recovery programs but also care for lower socio-economic long-term addicts, many of whom may be homeless. Whilst skill levels of volunteers may not always be to professional levels, the sheer number of volunteers and volunteered hours provides a major contribution to the care of addicts.

The not-for-profit organisations do not generally have the same resources and money to spend on recovery that the private sector might, per client. Parry, Kelliher, Mills, & Tyson (2005) found that service provision is similar in the voluntary and public sector. Whether the voluntary and public sector, provided by governments, produces results for addiction recovery that are as good as the private sector is difficult to assess. The private sector has fewer restrictions on how to treat a patient and the patients can often afford more care. It is also well known that the skill set in the voluntary sector is generally lower than in the private sector. The public sector eats up huge amounts of resources on administration and bureaucracy that would not be acceptable in the private sector. Furthermore, public and voluntary sectors are more likely to treat less motivated addicts, often from lower socio-economic groups, who are seeking recovery.

In a modern free-market economy where people want results faster with the least effort possible, drugs and alcohol have become perceived as a short-term, quick-fix solution to life's problems, along with fast food. Stich (2005) accuses the pharmaceutical companies of prospering from and propelling people to become dependent on many of their drugs. Doctors and purveyors of those drugs and alcohol often do not warn in advance of the danger of addiction that may lie ahead for many of those users, and users often become substance abusers.

A United Nations report noted the global production and distribution of the illicit drugs trade in 2003 was worth around $321 billion USD (Pollard, 2005). This is probably now much more considering China is now one of the major recreational drug manufacturers, and distribution pathways have become more sophisticated as drugs have become stronger and more compact, so are easier to transport. Hernandez (2013) reveals that the profits involved in these operations are vast, and protection of the industry literally leads to incredible protectionism, violence, corruption and murder by drug lords, who become multibillionaires.

Chouvy (2010) makes it clear many countries in the developing world are dependent on drug crops and manufacturing, such as opium and heroin. These include Mexico, Kyrgyzstan, Thailand, India, Iran and more. The manufacture of crops for or production of illicit drugs is a large part of their gross national product, so it is partly fundamental to their economy. Without those local economies these societies would have even more poverty. This is just as much the fault of developed countries which dominate international economics and trading as it is of developing countries' own governments to source alternative incomes. Kelly (2014) confirmed that governments, including the US government, support and protect certain drug lords who contribute toward domestic and foreign political change, so governments themselves have become involved in drug dealing, despite publicly promoting a 'war on drugs' policy.

The clinician who sits in ignorance of the world of drugs and alcohol will always see the trance the addict is living in as a form of pathology. The trance the addict is living in, however, is influenced by so many extraneous influences often beyond that person's previous ability to abstain. The client has not reached their 'Aha' moment about the influences that led them to addiction.

So we must look at the many influences that encourage the addicts and our clinical perceptions of drug use. It may not become drug abuse for every user but for some, the use can easily slip into dependence and abuse. This, of course, depends on the drug, its effects, availability, social acceptance and the personality of the individual.

Who perpetuates the alcohol and drug addiction trance:

- The client who enters into the beliefs around their dependence as it becomes a self-fulfilling prophecy
- Manufacturers of addictive substances who perpetuate the propaganda that you cannot do without the substance
- Governments that profit from the illicit drug trade
- Society that quantifies the separateness of the addict's undesirable behaviours
- Families who distance relatives with addiction problems
- The alcohol producers who advertise their products as chic and an opportunity to relax
- Pharmaceutical companies that produce and promote drugs as an answer to people's life problems
- Illicit drug dealers who market the attractiveness of their merchandise
- The medical establishment that tells people to take drugs to cure their life problems
- Clinicians and academics who classify addicts as sick

human beings with a pathology
- The legal system that turns addicts into criminals simply because they use drugs
- The penal system that often incarcerates and punishes addicts rather than offer them treatment
- The addiction recovery industry that at times makes more money out of addicts than people who recover from addiction
- The media that uses shocking and negative stories of substance use and addiction as titillation and headline-grabbing clickbait
- The bankers who move drug money around the world

As hypnotherapists helping the patient break their addictive trance, we cannot afford to appear as the bumbling therapists chanting the same route script to every addict that sits in our chair or lies on our couch. We must become the shaman to guide them to a life free from addiction that is deeply rewarding.

Whilst we must have our academic knowledge and clinical practice, most of all we need to establish a deep sense of rapport with addicts to lead them to a better life, to which we not only know the way, but that we live ourselves.

Allen, F. (2015). *Secret formula: The inside story of how Coca-Cola became the best-known brand in the world*. New York, NY: Open Road Media.

American Psychiatric Association. (2013). *Diagnostic and statistical manual of mental disorders* (5th ed.). Arlington, VA: Author.

Anderson, R. (2014, November 6). Pharmaceutical industry gets high on fat profits. *BBC News*. Retrieved from http://www.bbc.com/news

Angell, M. (2005). *The truth about the drug companies*. New York, NY: Random House.

Barry, M. (1989). *Ginsberg: A biography*. New York, NY: Simon & Schuster.

Blumenthal, P. (2012, February 1). Auction 2012: How drug companies game Washington. *The Huffington Post*. Retrieved from http://www.huffingtonpost.com/

Bonné, J. (2013). Lab-busting in the Northwest. *NBC News*. Retrieved from http://www.nbcnews.com/

Booth, M. (1999). *Opium: A history paperback*. New York, NY: St. Martin's Griffin.

Boyers, R., & Orrill, R. (1971). *Laing and anti-psychiatry*. New York, NY: Salamagundi Press.

Boztas, S. (2016, March 22). Netherlands doesn't have enough criminals to fill its prisons as crime to drop. *The Telegraph*. Retrieved from http://www.telegraph.co.uk/

Branley, A., & Scott, S. (2014, November 16). Anti-psychotic medication overprescribed to Australian children, experts say. *ABC Australia*. Retrieved from http://www.abc.net.au/

Breggin, P. (2013). *Psychiatric drug withdrawal: A guide for prescribers, therapists, patients and their families.* New York, NY: Springer.

Breggin, P. (2014). *Talking back to Prozac.* New York, NY: Open Road Media.

Brennan, I. (2016, April 14). Sex and crystal meth: The rise of chemsex. *ABC Australia.* Retrieved from http://www.abc.net.au/

Brown, M. (2017, January 10). David Bowie interview from 1996: "I have done just about everything that it's possible to do." *The Telegraph.* Retrieved from http://www.telegraph.co.uk/

Brown, P., & Gaines, S. (2002). *The love you make: An insider's story of the Beatles.* New York, NY: New American Library.

Cacciottolo, M. (2015, October 13). Saudi Arabia drinking: The risks expats take for a tipple. *BBC News.* Retrieved from http://www.bbc.com/news

Campos, D. J., & Overton, G. (Ed.). (2011). *The shaman and ayahuasca: Journeys to sacred realms.* (A. Roman, Trans.). Studio City, CA: Divine Arts.

Chalabi, M. (2016, April 20). The 'war on drugs' in numbers: A systematic failure of policy. *The Guardian.* Retrieved from https://www.theguardian.com

Chouvy, P.-A. (2010). *Opium: Uncovering the politics of the poppy.* Cambridge, MA: Harvard University Press.

Citizens Commission on Human Rights. (Producer). (2009). *Psychiatry: The marketing of madness: Are we all insane?* [Documentary]. Available from http://www.cchr.org/videos.html

Clarke, J. H. (1970). *The prescriber.* London, United Kingdom: Health Science Press.

Clear, J. (2016, April 22). Breaking bad habits: How Vietnam War veterans broke their heroin addictions. *The Huffington Post*. Retrieved from http://www.huffingtonpost.com/

Collin, M. (1997). *Altered state: The story of ecstacy culture and acid house*. London, United Kingdom: Serpent's Tail.

Dennis, B. (2015, November 3). Nearly 60 percent of Americans—the highest ever—are taking prescription drugs. *The Washington Post*. Retrieved from https://www.washingtonpost.com/

Donahue, J. (2006). A history of drug advertising: The evolving roles of consumers and consumer protection. *Milbank Quarterly, 84*(4), 659–699. doi:10.1111/j.1468-0009.2006.00464.x

Eisher, B. (1989). *Ecstacy: The MDMA story*. Berkeley, CA: Ronin.

Endredy, J. (2015). *Teaching of the peyote shamans: The five points of attention*. Rochester, VT: Park Street Press.

Finkelstein, J. B. (2008). Members of new FDA board tied to industry. *Journal of the National Cancer Institute, 100*(5), 296–297. doi:10.1093/jnci/djn051

Foster, C. (2011). *Wired for God*. London, United Kingdom: Hodder & Stoughton.

Gately, I. (2002). *Tobacco: A cultural history of how an exotic plant seduced civilization*. New York, NY: Grove Press.

Government of the Netherlands. (2017). *Toleration policy regarding soft drugs and coffee shops*. Retrieved from https://www.government.nl/topics/drugs/contents/toleration-policy-regarding-soft-drugs-and-coffee-shops

Greenfield, R. (2008). *Timothy Leary: A biography*. Orlando, FL: Harcourt.

Grof, S. (1980). *LSD psychotherapy*. Alameda, CA: Hunter House.

Guinn, J. (2014). *Manson: The life and times of Charles Manson.* New York, NY: Simon & Schuster.

Halbreich, U., Halbreich, J. A., & Jensvold, M. F. (1996). *Psychopharmacology and women: Sex, gender, and hormones.* Washington, D.C.: American Psychiatric Press.

Hames, G. (2012). *Alcohol in world history.* Abingdon, UK: Routledge.

Harrelson, W. J. (1969). *From fertility cult to worship.* New York, NY: Doubleday.

Hernandez, A. (2013). *The Mexican drug lords and their godfathers.* (I. Bruce & L. S. Fox, Trans.). New York, NY: Verso.

Holland, J. (Ed.). (2010). *The pot book: A complete guide to cannabis.* Rochester, VT: Park Street Press.

Huxley, L. (1991). *This timeless moment: A personal view of Aldous Huxley.* San Francisco, CA: Mercury House.

Ingraham, C. (2015, June 5). Why hardly anyone dies from a drug overdose in Portugal. *The Washington Post.* Retrieved from https://www.washingtonpost.com/

Ingraham, C. (2015, June 6). Portugal decriminalised drugs 14 years ago – and now hardly anyone dies from overdosing. *Independent.* Retrieved from http://www.independent.co.uk/

Kelly, E. (2015, January 5). Federal government cuts funding to ACT family drug and alcohol rehabilitation program at Karralika. *The Canberra Times.* Retrieved from http://www.canberratimes.com.au/

Kelly, M. B. (2014, January 13). CONFIRMED: The DEA struck a deal with Mexico's most notorious drug cartel. *Business Insider.* Retrieved from http://www.businessinsider.com/

Kilham, C. S. (2014). *The ayahuasca test pilots handbook:*

The essential guide to ayahuasca journeying. Berkeley, CA: North Atlantic Books.

Leary, T. (1990). *The politics of ecstasy.* Berkeley, CA: Ronin.

Lehmann-Haupt, C. (2001, November 11). Ken Kesey, author of 'Cuckoo's Nest,' who defined the psychedelic era, dies at 66. *The New York Times.* Retrieved from https://www. nytimes.com/

Letcher, A. (2008). *Shroom: A cultural history of the magic mushroom.* New York, NY: Harper Perennial.

Long, J., & Mongan, D. (2014). *Alcohol consumption in Ireland 2013.* Dublin, Ireland: Health Research Board. Retrieved from http://www.hrb.ie/uploads/tx_hrbpublications/ Alcohol_Consumption_in_Ireland_2013_web_version.pdf

Maragh, G. G., Howell, L. P., & McPherson, E. S. P. (2001). *The promised key: The original literary roots of Rastafari.* Hunlock Creek, PA: E World.

McKenna, T. (1992). *Food of the gods: The search for the original tree of knowledge.* New York, NY: Bantam Books.

McLellan, T. A. (2002). Have we evaluated addiction treatment correctly? Implications from a chronic care perspective. *Addiction, 97*(3), 249–252. doi:10.1046/j.1360-0443.2002.00127.x

McRae, B. (2001). *Tribal science: Brains, beliefs, and bad ideas.* Brisbane, Australia: University of Queensland Press.

Moore, T. J. (1998). *Prescription for disaster: The hidden danger in your medicine cabinet.* New York, NY: Simon & Schuster.

Munro, D. (2015, April 27). Inside the $35 billion addiction treatment industry. *Forbes.* Retrieved from http://www.forbes.com.

Musto, D. F. (Ed.). (2002). *One hundred years of heroin*. Westport, CT: Praeger.

O'Hara, M. (2012, June 26). Charities are providing drugs and alcohol services in place of the NHS. *The Guardian*. Retrieved from https://www.theguardian.com/

Ohler, N. (2016). *Blitzed*. London, United Kingdom: Penguin Books.

Okrent, D. (2011). *Last call: The rise and fall of prohibition*. New York, NY: Scribner.

Owen, A. R. G. (1971). *Hysteria, hypnosis, and healing: The work of J-M. Charcot*. New York, NY: Garrett Publications.

Parry, E., Kelliher, C., Mills, T., & Tyson, S. (2005). Comparing HRM in the voluntary and public sectors. *Personnel Review, 34*(5), 588–602. doi:10.1108/00483480510612530

Pollard, N. (2005, June 30). UN report puts world's illicit drug trade at estimated $321b. *Boston.com*. Retrieved from https://www.boston.com/

Potterton, D. (Ed.). (1983). *Culpeper's color herbal*. Marlow, United Kingdom: W. Foulsham.

Rasmussen, N. (2011). Medical science and the military: The Allies' use of amphetamine during World War II. *Journal of Interdisciplinary History, 42*(2), 203–233. doi:10.2174/1745017901208010110

Reynar, J. (2008, December 13). May the spirit be with you. *The Observer*. Retrieved from https://www.theguardian.com/observer

Saunders, N. (1997). *Ecstasy reconsidered*. London, United Kingdom: Author.

Smith, G. A. (Producer), & Knezev, S. (Director). (2012). *American Addict* [Motion picture]. United States: Pain MD Productions.

Stamets, P. (1996). *Psilocybin mushrooms of the world: An identification guide.* Berkeley, CA: Ten Speed Press.

Stevens, J. (1993). *Storming heaven: LSD and the American dream.* London, United Kingdom: Flamingo.

Stich, R. (2005). *Drugging America: A Trojan horse* (2nd ed.). Alamo, CA: Silverpeak Enterprises.

Streatfeild, D. (2002). *Cocaine: A definitive history.* London, United Kingdom: Virgin Books.

Szasz, T. (2008). *Psychiatry: The science of lies.* Syracuse, NY: Syracuse University Press.

Tasca. C., Rapetti, M., Carta, M. G., & Fadda, B. (2012). Women and hysteria in the history of mental health. *Clinical Practice & Epidemiology in Mental Health, 8,* 110–119.

T. W. (2015, April 28). Which countries have the death penalty for drug smuggling? *The Economist.* Retrieved from http://www.economist.com/

United Nations Office on Drugs and Crime. (2012). *World drug report 2012.* Retrieved from https://www.unodc.org/documents/data-and-analysis/WDR2012/WDR_2012_web_small.pdf

U.S. Department of Health and Human Services, Federal Food and Drug Administration. (n.d.). *Frequently asked questions about the FDA drug approval process.* Retrieved from https://www.fda.gov/drugs/resourcesforyou/specialfeatures/ucm279676.htm

U.S. Department of Justice, Bureau of Justice Statistics. (2016). *Prisoners in 2015* (NCJ Publication No. 250229). Retrieved from https://www.bjs.gov/content/pub/pdf/p15.pdf

The Drugs You May Meet in Your Practice and Their Effects

I tell students that you must know your drugs and intoxicating substances. Coming to a client naive is never acceptable for a clinician. You are getting paid as the expert, so you need to be an expert. Even if you work in a not-for-profit organisation as a volunteer without payment, you have a duty to be the expert when a client sits before you. You may never have encountered any of these intoxicating substances personally, but you need an academic knowledge of them.

I have listed some of the drugs used by clients you may see in your practice but in many ways I am just skimming the surface. There are too many drugs and alcoholic drinks to cover within this book and new drugs are coming onto the streets and the market each day, so you will need to keep up to date with all the drugs and alcohol people are using.

Cultural drugs

Ayahuasca (hallucinogenic, oral administration) is the shamanic drug made of a tea from the *Banisteriopsis caapi* vine used by native shamans in the South American jungle, particularly the Peruvian Amazon. Its medicinal properties induce vomiting and diarrhoea, which can rid the body of worms and parasites. The documentary *Stepping into the Fire* (Velez & Evison, 2011) shows that many people from around the world go to South America to discover for themselves a life beyond this material plane, and undergo a transcendental journey. A few people are reported to have died on an ayahuasca journey. Shamans also mix it with other plants, with different shamans mixing different brews.

Metzner (2005) says users have described ayahuasca as having a deeply psychologically cathartic effect. As a hallucinogenic drug, it also breaks down the containment of memories and, while under its influence, people may review their lives and behaviours. For many people it is a transformational experience that may help them overcome depression, and can set people on a different life course after use. People go to South America, not only for spiritual transformation, but also to find ways to overcome their physical illnesses. Ayahuasca is called the teaching plant by shamans and used as healing medicine, with effects that last anything from overnight to several days.

Peyote (*Lophophore williamsii*, hallucinogenic, oral administration) is a sacred traditional plant medicine. It is taken from a southern North American small spineless cactus that contains psychoactive alkaloids, including mescaline. In traditional medicine it is used for toothache, rheumatism, childbirth, breast pain and other uses. It is also used for ceremonial and personal spiritual exploration under shamanic guidance and in some churches where cultural crossover occurs with Western Christianity. It has been used for spiritual purposes by North American and Mexican natives for more than 5000 years, as far as anthropologists can tell. One of its native language names is 'Divine Messenger'. It is considered a window into the spiritual world. When Caucasian Western culture arrived in America, peyote was made illegal until legislation recognised native Americans' rights to practise their religion (Anderson, 1996).

Ratsch (2005) advises dosing is difficult to estimate as the strength of the cactus and its psychoactive constituents are varied. Little button parts of the cactus are eaten. The effects last from 10 to 12 hours but in large doses the person can be hallucinating for days. Users report its effects can be deeply insightful, introspective, reflective, spiritual and metaphysical, with hallucinations occurring in all the senses. Since it is still deeply associated with shamanic use, at the time of writing this book, it has not yet crossed over into recreational drug use in the mainstream. It is, however, used internationally in experimental and shamanic psychotherapy. It is also used by people experimenting with psychoactive drugs.

Dos Santos (2011) maintains that, as with any psychoactive drug use, over-use can result in psychosis. It is also important to remember that people with psychiatric or psychological disturbances may not be able to handle the kinds of psychodynamic issues that may surface during a peyote trip. As the psychiatrist Milton Erickson suggested, the unconscious mind hides things from the conscious mind that it does not think it is able to handle. So within the native shamanic environment users are guided, but when the drug is taken in non-traditional environments individuals can have quite scary psychodynamic revelations and hallucinations, which they may be unable to handle. This can result in psychosis.

Mescaline (3,4,5-trimethoxyphenethylamine, hallucinogenic, oral administration) is a psychedelic alkaloid present in the *Lophophore williamsii* cactus but also in other cactaceae plants. Small amounts are found in the *Fabaceae* (bean) family, including *Acacia berlandieri*. The San Pedro cactus (*Echinopsis pachanoi*) contains the highest level of mescaline in the world and is made into a powerful brew to be drunk. Psychederic (2015) describes it as a powerful psychedelic with crossover effects to peyote, and of course peyote also contains mescaline. Its use is culturally connected to shamanic rituals in Mexico and South America, particularly Peru, where it has been associated with a pilgrimage to a sacred lake for over 5000 years.

Since it can be synthesised in the laboratory, mescaline is being used in the Western world and people are using it as a recreational drug. It can initially lead to vomiting. Olive (2007) advises that some people may be energised and others may seem subdued when they are hallucinating, which lasts from several hours to days according to the dose.

It is important that people taking the substance have a carer looking after them while they are tripping. Constant use can lead to drug-induced psychosis.

Kava kava (*Piper methysticum*, oral administration and sometimes extracts are smoked) is an extract from the root of the plant that has been used by Pacific Ocean cultures for thousands of years as traditional medicine. The active ingredients are kavalactones. It is made into a drink but also into pills or herbal extracts. Sahelian (1998) lauds its use as a sedative, anti-anxiety, muscle relaxant, anaesthetic and sleep medication. It is used in commercial drinks in all levels of society in the Pacific region. Traditionally it is prepared by either chewing, pounding or grinding the root.

There are many different strains of kava kava, with some containing more psychoactive alkaloids than others. In cultures such as Vanuatu, growing is strictly regulated, with only the noble strain being allowed to be exported. Rose (2009) reports it produces a state of relaxation and calmness and is used in herbalism as a calmative, although as a medical herbalist I find it too depressive for patients.

Like alcohol it can produce an initial chatty period followed by sleepiness, with diminished cognitive and reactive abilities. Memory also seems to be enhanced with taking the drink but it is stronger when the extract is smoked. Reports of hallucinations from taking large amounts suggest these occur when other substances have been added to the brew.

Continuous use can lead to addiction and diminished cognitive abilities. Reports of liver damage are generally attributed, both by individuals and by manufacturers of kava kava pills, to using the wrong strain and part of the plant (Bone & Mills, 2013).

Scopolamine (Hyocine, a tropane alkaloid, 'Devil's breath', snorted through the nose, removes free will, creates amnesia) comes from the borrachero shrub, a common plant in Colombia, South America, and is a native cultural drug that was used in traditional medicine, shamanic journeys and rituals. The seeds are ground into powder and the active extracted chemical is burandanga. Jimson weed also contains scopolamine and is spread across the US continent. Graybiel, Cramer, & Wood (1982) investigate its use in medicine where it decreases nerve signals and secretions from the stomach and intestines, reducing nausea and vomiting. It is administered to treat blockages of the intestine, severe breathing disorders and narrow-angle glaucoma. It has also been used in transdermal form for sea sickness and post-operative sickness and nausea.

Scopolamine has crossed over into the public domain in South America as a recreational drug during the past decade, where its profound effects have led to social problems. Whilst it is a hallucinogenic drug, it also has the strange quality of removing the free will of the person, so they do whatever other people order them to do. It also creates amnesia, so afterwards, when the person is no longer under the effects of the drug, they cannot remember what happened during the altered state (Khakpai, Nasehi, Haeri-Rohani, Eidi, & Zarrindast, 2012). It is very easy to administer as a dust that can simply be blown into someone's face as they inhale, dropped into a drink or it can be absorbed from impregnated paper or cloth. Peatfield & Villilón (2013) note it has been used as a date rape drug.

The controversy that has arisen with the drug is that it is being used by criminals, and there are reports of people waking up in hotels with organs missing that were harvested and sold. The criminal may have cleared out the victim's bank account, but on recovery, the victim has lost several days and has no memory of that happening. Over 50,000 people a year are affected in Colombia where it is frequently used in nightclubs or bars for criminal intent. Samuel (2015) describes how it has been used as far afield as Paris in conning and robbing people.

Petrol (depressant, hallucinogenic, snorted through the nose) is common in more culturally and economically disadvantaged communities. The petrol is generally stolen and siphoned out of cars. The aromatic vapours cause a high. Addiction happens very quickly and can last for decades, with people having to sniff every few hours, even waking up at night to sniff. Brain damage occurs, particularly in teenagers who have developing brains. Campbell (2016) reports that sniffing rates in Indigenous communities in Australia diminished by 88% since the introduction of low aromatic unleaded fuel 10 years ago. However, in other cultures petrol sniffing is still a problem.

Glue (depressant, hallucinogenic, snorted through the nose) and **industrial chemicals and deodorants** are popular in more culturally and economically disadvantaged communities, particularly with young children. The volatile vapours or gases are concentrated and cause a high, with people ending up using all day long. Cooper, Newton & Reed (1985) illuminate how people can become addicted for many years, resulting in mental deterioration and possible brain damage.

Flakka/flaka/floka (α-Pyrrolidinopentiophenone, also known as alpha-pyrrolidinovalerophenone, α-PVP, alpha-PVP, O-2387, β-keto-prolintane, Prolintanone, or Desmethyl Pyrovalerone, 'Gravel', 'the Devil's Drug', 'Zombie', snorted through the nose) is a powerful stimulant and hallucinogenic that creates extreme psychosis and psychotic breaks. It is a synthetic version of an amphetamine-like stimulant in the cathinone class called alpha-PVP. It gives an instant high that is so profound it induces hallucination, psychosis, paranoia and derangement, complete withdrawal of inhibitions, extreme strength, aggression, excited delirium, and total suspension of reality testing. It is dubbed the 'insanity drug' as people can appear completely deranged, and are sometimes involved in murders and suicide. Some users jump out of buildings, in front of cars and through car windows. It has spread across the US, with more than 600 cases recorded in 2014 (Glatter, 2015) and is now being seen in other countries. Scaccia (2016) in *Rolling Stone* investigated its effects in Florida where doses can cost as little as $3.

Phencyclidine (PCP, angel dust, hallucinogenic, depressant, snorted, oral administration, injected or absorbed through skin) is a drug that has been common in America. It is a very powerful drug where people get so intoxicated that they have no control over their bodies and minds. It was developed and marketed as an anaesthetic in the 1950s but, due to uncontrollable hallucinations, was deemed so dangerous that it was taken off the market in 1965. On the streets it comes in many forms including powder, crystals, tablets, capsules or liquids. Morris & Wallach (2014) find its effects may ensue in about two minutes when injected, but when taken orally, up to one hour and last from four to 48 hours depending on dosage and quality.

PCP is a thought and mood deregulator. It is a dissociative, sedating drug so people are unable to orientate themselves to the world and conduct reality testing. It also has addictive qualities. The person experiences superhuman strength, sexual prowess, grandiose delusions, involuntary body movements, impaired ability to remember, impaired ability to make logical decisions, and speech problems. Suicidal thoughts may occur in some people, along with flashbacks and delusional thinking. Colourful and all-engrossing hallucinations happen during the intense parts of the experience. People can be found in public places completely unaware of where they are or what is happening. Bev & Patel's review (2007) has shown the possibility of brain damage in constant users.

GHB (gamma-hydroxybutyric acid, also known as 4-hydroxy-butanoic acid, hallucinogenic, depressant, oral and liquid administration) has been used as a general anaesthetic and treatment for narcolepsy and is a precursor to GABA (gamma-aminobutyric acid), glutamate, and glycine in areas of the brain. It acts on the GHB receptor and it is a weak agonist at the GABAB receptor. Produced during the process of fermentation, it is in wines and beers and is a central nervous system depressant and intoxicant with effects similar to alcohol and MDMA, producing euphoria, disinhibition, sexual enhancement and increased empathy. At higher doses, GHB produces nausea, drowsiness, depressed breathing, visual disturbances, agitation, amnesia, unconsciousness and death. It is frequently used on the club scene and can become highly addictive with regular use. McDaniel & Miotto (2001) found that many of the side effects are due to the use of large amounts on a regular basis and that such use can cause addictive symptoms. As far back as 1995 Ferrara, Tedeschi, Frison, & Rossi (1995) reported fatalities, particularly with multiple drug users.

Anabolic steroids (anabolic-androgenic steroids [AAS], muscle builder, oral administration or injection) are used by athletes, body builders and members of the public to increase muscle mass, bulk up the body frame and build strength. They increase protein within the cells, particularly muscle cells. They include natural steroidal androgens and synthetic substances. In medicine, anabolic steroids are used in endocrinology to increase or supplement the effects of testosterone or in cases when growth hormones are not operating, as well as in sex and gender reaffirming medicine. In many places they are illegal and are traded on the black market in gym locker rooms. There is particular social pressure in many walks of life for men to look unrealistically strong and muscularly developed as a sign of masculinity, as shown in the documentary *STEROIDS – Anabolic STEROIDS* *in Sports and Bodybuilding* (Lofft, 2015). Also, there is pressure for female athletes to be stronger and perform well in order to win in their sport, so some of them will take steroids.

These substances are part of the designer body movement and once someone starts to take them, they may believe they will have to keep taking them, either to retain their competitive edge or because they do not want to lose their body bulk. Some body builders inject steroids straight into their muscles. Addiction in the medical context is psychological, and complications can occur, including testicular shrinkage, impotence, cardiovascular disease, liver failure, muscles becoming too large for their sheaths, memory loss, dizziness, drowsiness, and mood disorders including depression, anxiety and aggression. Fratie, Busardo, Cipolloni, De Dominicis, & Fineschi (2015) report over-use can sometimes lead to sudden cardiac death (SCD).

Nutmeg ([genus *Myristica*)], **Cinnamon** [genus *Cinnamomum*], **Catnip** [genus *Nepeta cataria*], hallucinogenic, smoked, snorted in large amounts) are used by younger people with little money to get high. Ground nutmeg or cinnamon can be snorted and give a hallucinogenic trip that can last from eight hours to three days depending on the dose. The oil can be extracted and placed on catnip and smoked. Conely (2010) notes its side effects include nausea, vomiting, heart palpitations, dehydration, aches and pains, delirium, haunting hallucinations, depression and, in cases of overdose, death.

Herbal drugs have been touted as safer options by sellers as they may be derived from many plant substances. This, however, is quite misleading. Just because these substances are not synthetically manufactured in laboratories, are extractions from plants and not on governments' legal controlled substances lists does not mean they will not cause addiction or have extreme side effects. In the Channel Islands, the *Guernsey Press* ("Legal highs trade has slowed to a trickle," 2016) reported that the government had taken measures with the Border Agency to stop packages from being sent through the mail containing these substances, due to the social problems they cause, particularly in the young.

Amphetamine sulphate (speed, stimulant, snorted, oral administration or injection) is commonly referred to as 'speed' due to its stimulant effects that can last several hours. It is usually snorted in lines through a rolled-up bank note or straw straight into the nostrils. Over the years it has been highly popular on the club scene to give people a euphoric high and the stamina to dance all night long. The comedown leads to tiredness, insomnia and a sense of exhaustion. Generally used as a weekend party drug, it can lead to addiction, extreme weight loss, reduction of body fat, chronic insomnia, psychosis, paranoia and delusional states. Barr, Panenka, MacEwan, Thornton, Lang, Honer, & Lecomte (2006) found that regular use can lead to considerable reduction in cognitive abilities and emotional instability.

Crystal Methamphetamine (stimulant, oral administration, snorted, injected, smoked), also known as 'ice' or just 'meth', is cheaper than cocaine and three and a half times more powerful, with a single hit keeping someone high for six to 12 hours. It is the pure form of amphetamine, as opposed to common street speed which is often cut with other substances. It was developed a hundred years ago and used in the Second World War to keep soldiers pumped and ready to kill without having to stop to eat. The reason it has become so prolific is that it is simple to make in anyone's kitchen or garden shed from anhydrous ammonia from farm chemicals and pseudoephedrine from cough medicine. This means anyone can set themselves up as a manufacturer and dealer. The premises used for this become impregnated for future inhabitants and need forensic decontamination. In the documentary *Crystal Meth – The World's Most Dangerous Drugs* (Loeffler & Yates, 2006), it can be seen how users' mental and physical deterioration and addiction occur very quickly as people become delusional and disorientated.

Meth increases dopamine, norepinephrine and cortisol and subdues the decision-making parts of the brain. Users perceive themselves as stronger, euphoric, and energetic, with a greater sense of endurance and tolerance. However, people deteriorate, often sliding into psychosis so quickly that they are unable to work, and become involved in crime. Meth combines the hyperactivity of cocaine with the hallucinations of psychedelic drugs. Most of the world's meth users are in Asia as the drug is used to help people stay awake for days so they can work longer hours to get ahead in life. Sim (2016) exposes us to violent images in some of these countries, such as the Philippines, which have large social problems, and the Filipino government started to become involved in murdering users and dealers.

The deterioration that occurs includes extreme loss of weight, advanced ageing, loss of teeth, arteriosclerosis, cardiovascular incidents, gastrointestinal disturbances, aggression, paranoia, anxiety, depression, mood disorders, and extreme dark and haunting delusional hallucinations that can last for days at a time. Braswell (2006) says users experience a crawling sensation over their skin, called meth bugs, and begin to pick at their skin, creating sores and wounds.

Cocaine ([methyl (1R,2R,3S,5S)-3- (benzoyloxy)-8-methyl-8-azabicyclo[3.2.1] octane-2-carboxylate], stimulant, snorted or injected, also known as 'coke' or 'snow') is a class A drug that was perfected in 1860 by a refinement process from the stimulant from the coca plant. It was originally used as the first chemical anaesthetic. Cocaine works by inhibiting the re-uptake of serotonin, norepinephrine and dopamine. The appeal for drug users is that it is a popular, instant, highly effective stimulant, even though possession can be an imprisonable offence. The coca plant's mild stimulant, when processed in the laboratory, is converted into a highly effective pure white crystal drug. It causes an increase in dopamine and the person feels good, confident, excited, almost invincible, as the brain floods with dopamine and norepinephrine. In the documentary *How Drugs Work Episode 3 – Cocaine* (Fletcher, 2011), we can see the party culture that is a typical depiction of cocaine as a social drug.

Nestler (2005) suggests users can take cocaine on weekends, a few times a month, or addicts may take it several times a day. It is both a party drug that increases nerve cell connections and is perceived as a drug that increases concentration and performance, giving the sense of euphoria, and decreases hunger. Cocaine increases sexual appetite and blood flow to the penis, retards ejaculation, and heightens sexual perception, but reduces the decision-making part of the brain. Taking too much gives rise to impotency. The high generally lasts from 30 to 40 minutes before the user has to take more to retain it. It dramatically increases the circulating norepinephrine, cortisol, blood pressure, pulse, and heart rate, and increases the risk of heart attack by 20 times, at any age, rendering the heart permanently damaged. Constant snorting users can suffer collapse of the nose, causing a nasal septal perforation through the bridge of the nasal tissue. Use can also lead to holes in different parts of the oral nasal cavities and structures that may have to be repaired by surgery. Constant use or over-use can lead to lack of sleep, insomnia, respiratory problems, depression, anxiety, irritability, aggression, paranoia, panic attacks and a schizoid break. The UN estimated that more than 60 million people around the globe took cocaine in 2008 (United Nations Office on Drugs and Crime, 2008).

Crack cocaine (stimulant, smoked, also known as 'rocks' or 'crack') is a form of cocaine that is smoked rather than snorted, so absorption is through the lungs via a crack pipe. The high the person experiences is faster and more intense than regular cocaine. It is stronger when smoked, therefore is much more addictive than regular cocaine, and addiction sets in faster too. Antai-Otong (2006) says the addict becomes so obsessed with the drug they cease to eat well, shower or take care of themselves, leading to a profound deterioration in physical and mental state, with 25% of myocardial infarctions in the US being due to cocaine overdose.

Ecstasy (3,4-Methylenedioxymethamphetamine, MDMA, oral, nasal, anal administration, snorted, smoked or may be injected, also known as 'E', 'X' or 'Molly') has become a popular drug over the past 30 years, producing fashion and culture all of its own. It was originally devised in Germany in 1912 and was intended to be used as a blood clotting agent. Kalant (2001) describes it as an amphetamine derivative with properties of mescaline, although it is not a hallucinogenic. Clinically it has been experimented with for psychotherapeutic purposes to treat post-traumatic stress disorder (PTSD).

It is particularly popular with people from about 18 to 30 who are involved in the club and dance scenes. It is known as the 'love drug' because people become highly social and friendly after taking it. Different batches come with all sorts of names such as 007, white diamonds, love doves, Mitsubishi and hundreds more. People begin to make friends and be sociable with complete strangers as the hormone serotonin is released, building up in the blood. This then triggers the release of oxytocin from the brain, which is the hormone that helps people bond with others. The brain also produces dopamine, which controls movement, so users feel full of high energy and want to dance. Collin (2010) charted ecstasy's journey as a club drug, noting it can come in pill form or crystal, with people sometimes taking three to seven pills in a night, often at weekends as a party drug.

Its effects begin 30 to 45 minutes after ingestion but almost instantly when injected. The feelings of elation, excitement, euphoria and feeling in the party mood last between three to six hours and is often referred to as 'buzzing'. The documentary *How Drugs Work Episode 2 – Ecstasy* (Fletcher, 2011) warns that the contents vary wildly and many ecstasy tablets being sold do not actually contain MDMA but substitute drugs such as the psychiatric drug m-chlorophenylpiperazine, or methamphetamine.

Rising norepinephrine (noradrenaline) leads to extreme exertion and dehydration, so people have to drink a lot of water. In some cases people retain high levels of water in the blood, urination is reduced, the brain swells in the skull and the person dies. Also hyperthermia can occur when the hypothalamus fails to regulate body temperature, causing organs to shut down, particularly the liver. Some people's livers do not have the ability to detoxify the drug. After several doses the body is unable to release more serotonin and the person crashes, is exhausted, and it may take several days before serotonin levels return to normal. Continual use over many months can lead to psychosis, anxiety, depression, panic attacks, irritability, loss of sleep, loss of memory, lack of focus, adrenal exhaustion, lowered immune system, and thyroid and hypothalamus disruption. Some people use ecstasy with other drugs at the same time but it is unusual for ecstasy users to get pure ecstasy from their dealers, as sources may well be cut with something else. Potas, Gordon, and Conrad (2009) reviewed cases of complications and psychosis occurring in some people from a single use.

Opium (Lachryma papaveris, depressant, hallucinogenic, oral administration, smoked, transdermal) is generally smoked in different parts of the world through a pipe as a recreational drug. According to the documentary *Afghan Overdose: Inside the Opium Trade* (RT Documentary, 2015), in Afghanistan alone there is an estimated 150,000 opium addicts, including whole families of three or more generations. Opium is contained in the head of the poppy flower that grows all over the world and is particularly farmed in developing countries. Through cultivation programs and cross-fertilisation, the phenanthrene alkaloids morphine, codeine and thebaine have been increased to make the crop stronger. Medically opium is used to treat pain and coughs. The dried latex contains around 12% of the analgesic alkaloid morphine, which, although used for thousands of years for pain control and inducing sleep, is highly addictive.

When taking the drug, the person feels very relaxed and disorientated, with warm, comfortable feelings. According to the documentary *Opium in China* (Sun, 2015), for thousands of years the drug was used in China as a medicine but then became a problem in the 19th century when opium smoking houses brought Chinese society to a crisis before the drug was restricted and then banned in the 1940s under the communist regime. Opium can be highly addictive and has the side effect of depressing the breathing response. People tend to lose interest in life and may sell everything they have to get their supply. Buss (2006) explains that opium induces constipation, nausea, vomiting, anxiety, blurred vision, confusion, disorientation and a coma, as well as many other symptoms.

Heroin (3,6-Diacetylmorphine, diamorphine, depressant, hallucinogenic, injected or smoked – chasing the dragon – also known as 'smack' or 'gear') is the processed opiate from the dried latex of the poppy plant (*Papaver somniferous*). It is one of the world's most widely used and highly addictive drugs. Most governments class it a schedule one drug and it is occasionally used in medicine for pain relief. The poppy is one of the biggest cash crops in the world, with whole economies in some countries depending on the revenue heroin brings from international smuggling. Heroin is far less bulky and easier to smuggle than its derivative opium form and, when made, becomes an off-white salt heroin hydrochloride. *National Geographic* shows us the huge scale of international smuggling operations (Hewes, 2014).

When injected or smoked, it gives an instant sense of calm

and distance from the world, releasing a flood of dopamine in the brain, numbing the body's pain centres, as the person experiences derealisation. It shuts down functions of the frontal lobe of the brain including the decision-making processes, although users describe its effects as a security blanket. All batches tend to have different purity and strengths, thereby making the effects highly unpredictable. Again, *National Geographic* shows us how addicts also often use a lot of other drugs, so when presenting for rehabilitation they generally have multiple addictions (Hewes, 2014).

One of the major problems that arises with heroin abuse is that the drug is often cut with other substances by dealers to bulk up the product to a higher price per kilo, so the addict rarely gets pure heroin. This leads to the most common cause of death being overdose. Complications involve strong addiction, HIV and hepatitis C needle contamination from shared needles, collapsing veins from over-use of constant injection sites, gum shrinkage, loss of teeth and hair, malnutrition, memory loss, constipation, gastrointestinal problems, breathing problems, impotence, collapse of mucosal tissue of the nose when snorted, heart and blood vessel problems, boils and abscesses, organ collapse, and vesicular blockage from the user failing to properly dissolve the powder in order for it to be injected. There are also extremely high levels of mental health and psychological problems among heroin abusers, including depression, anxiety, sociopathy and antisocial behaviours, which may have existed before addiction or as result of addiction. As Warner-Smith, Darke, Linskey, & Hall (2001) note, ultimately the major problem heroin abusers experience is death by overdose due to varying quality of supply and the addict's inability to monitor usage.

Krokodil (Desomorphine opioid derivative, hallucinogenic, stimulant, injection, also known as the Zombie drug and the flesh eater drug) is a highly destructive drug that has swept across Russia from 2002, affecting tens of thousands of people. It spread to America in 2013 and has appeared in other places throughout the world. According to the documentary *Krokodil: Russia's Deadliest Drug* (Vice, 2012), in the Russian city of Novokuznetsk it is estimated that more than 20% of the population are addicted to heroin, many of whom are also using Krokodil. It can be made from Caffetin, formic acid, eyedrops containing tropicamide and gasoline, and then cooking it down. It is cheaper than heroin and often not illegal. The *Vice* documentary shows us how heroin addicts often progress to Krokodil and die within two years.

This drug is so addictive that many people who take it never recover. Because it is so cheap, easy to make and highly addictive, it particularly devastates the lower socio-economic communities. The high reached is extremely fast, particularly after injection, but lasts only a short time. The most notable feature of this drug is that it shuts down peripheral blood vessels, causing necrosis of the skin, which begins to look like crocodile scales. The skin tissue then drops off the body, leaving fully-exposed muscles, tendons, nerves, blood vessels and bone. Internal organs begin to collapse, including the brain, with loss of speech and motor skills before death ensues. *The Huffington Post* (Jauregui, 2014) reported extreme concern by the US government as the drug began to infiltrate North American communities.

Cannabis (*Cannabis savita* or *Cannabis indica*, smoked, oral or anal ingestion, also known as 'dope', 'blow' or 'weed') comes from hemp. Hemp is one of the most useful plants on the planet. Its seeds are highly nutritious and contain all the essential amino acids needed to build the body. Hemp bale is an amazingly strong building material that is virtually fire-resistant. There are hundreds of strains of cannabis and more are being developed by growers by cross-fertilisation. Each has various effects on the body, brain and mind. Medicinally its administration is useful, when the cannabinoids (CBD) are high and the tetrahydrocannabinol (THC) is low, in reducing seizures, particularly from epilepsy, eliminating shaking in Parkinson's-like disorders and pain, and increasing appetite in patients with cancer. Fine (2014) reports a global increase in production as the many industrial and medical qualities of the plant are embraced.

Hemp contains the psychoactive drug THC which is a sedative but also a hallucinogenic in high concentrations, creating depersonalisation and derealisation, otherwise known as being high. The plant also contains CBD which reduces the effects of the THC. Some strains have high THC and low CBD and vice versa. Strains with high THC can lead to addiction and breakdown of mental processes. Kuhn, Swartzwelder, and Wilson (2014) cite the problem that has arisen is that cannabis dealers are selling recreational users strains with ever-increasingly higher THC, particularly when the plant is grown hydroponically which can increase the THC by five times or more.

Cannabis Weed (depressant, stimulant, hallucinogenic, analgesic, smoked, also known as 'grass', 'pot', 'weed', 'smoke', 'ganja', Blanche) is taken from the flowering buds of the female plant, which has the highest level of THC, and dried ready for use. It is then smoked in a rolled cigarette (known as a 'joint' or 'reefer') mixed with tobacco or in some cases it is smoked neat. It can also be smoked in a pipe or bong. To extract the THC for cooking it needs to be heated with a carrier oil so it becomes bioavailable to the body.

Cannabis Oil (depressant, stimulant, hallucinogenic, analgesic, smoked, oral and anal administration, sometimes known as 'hash oil') is a sticky resin containing cannabinoids, such as THC and CBD, which has been extracted from the cannabis plant. A separation process is used to remove the resins from cannabis flowers via a solvent extraction process. It can be mixed with tobacco to smoke for an instant high or used in cooking cakes, flapjacks or brownies. It can take about 45 minutes to get high but the effects last longer than when smoked.

Cannabis Resin (hashish, depressant, stimulant, hallucinogenic, analgesic, smoked, oral administration) is made from the dried resin of the leaf stems and buds of the plant and dried into a hard, lump-like chocolate consistency. To use it, the hard resin needs to be burned with a flame and then crumbled for use or used directly in a pipe or bong. It may also be used in cooking.

There is a huge push in many cultures to re-legalise cannabis, which is driven by users, decriminalisation advocates and large corporations that are now seeking commercial opportunities to produce and manufacture it. Much of that argument is based on its efficacious potential but also the argument that it is not an addictive substance. However, in the documentary *How Drugs Work Episode 1 – Cannabis* (Fletcher, 2011), it is easy to see that people do have cannabis addictions over many decades which can cause psychosis, paranoia, and schizoid-type behaviours.

LSD (D-lysergic acid and (+)-lysergic acid, commonly known as acid) is a hallucinogenic drug produced by the ergot fungus. It can also be produced synthetically in a laboratory. In many countries it is an illegal drug. Some physicians have been involved in its use as a form of pharmacological psychotherapy. We can see from the work of researchers such as Bender, Goldschmidt, Sankar, & Freedman (1968) that it gained a bad reputation when clinicians were experimenting on patients without their permission, including children.

Hofman (2009) tells us as a powerful hallucinogenic LSD can give rise to both positive and negative hallucinations in any modality. The internal experiential psychedelic journey that is produced is known as a trip and there has been considerable experimentation using it in psychotherapeutic treatment, which has produced varied results.

Many artists and intellectuals have used LSD for inspiration, including writers, musicians and even computer designers. It produces profound experiences of altered perception, and visio-spatial distortion and can alter all perception of the five senses.

Stafford (1993) writes that since the results vary greatly, manufacturers give batches many different names such as 'Superman' or 'Strawberry fields'. The average trip may last from six to eight hours depending on the product's qualities and the amount taken. Dosage can change dramatically as it is generally not well monitored because it is manufactured illegally. Manufacturers tend to use lower doses nowadays rather than the large doses that were often available in the 1960s during the psychedelic revolution. Sometimes when people have taken large amounts, they hallucinate for a week or more. Since batches can vary wildly, the effects are varied according to strength, dosage and personal susceptibility. A person can have a good trip, or at times, a bad trip, depending on their psychological make-up. LSD has the ability to open up parts of the psyche not typically accessible during the normal conscious state.

For some people an acid trip is life-changing, enjoyable and revelational. For others it is more than their psychological makeup can handle and can cause haunting trauma. Since LSD suspends reality testing, people can be unaware of physical dangers and some have jumped out of windows and off buildings because they believed they could fly. For this reason people tend to take LSD in groups where often one person, who has not dropped acid, can monitor the safety of the others. Strassman (1984), in reviewing the literature, clearly shows repeated usage can cause severe psychosis, psychotic decompression, depression, paranoia and schizophrenic-like experiences.

N-Bomb (25I-NBOMe, derivative of the substituted phenethylamine psychedelic 2C-I, inhaled, smoked, oral administration, injected) is a synthetic hallucinogen sold as an alternative to LSD or mescaline. It is sold as a powder, liquid or soaked into blotting paper, and is placed under the tongue for sub-lingual or buccal absorption but creates no effects if swallowed. There are several variations of the drug, with the most common at the moment being called 251 and all may be sold as legal LSD. It is so toxic that handlers must wear masks and protective clothing to avoid fatal doses through ingestion. Users report that they felt as if their mind was being torn apart and they can become violent and deranged. *News.com.au* reported the drug had been suspected as being responsible for several deaths on the Gold Coast in Australia ("Drug 'n-bomb' that caused GC overdoses", 2016).

Psilocybin mushrooms (magic mushrooms, shrooms, hallucinogenic, oral administration) contain the compounds psilocybin and psilocin, which are psychedelics. Stamets (1996) tells us these have been used since the beginning of time by humans all over the world and run to more than a hundred species with varying effects. The Ancient Greeks referred to them as creating the 'divine within', and used them for spiritual development. Their use was mainly entheogenic until the 1950s when the Western world began to take notice of them. They have been experimented with for psychotherapeutic purposes and were made popular in the 1960s by their use in the hippie movement. A trip comes on around an hour after ingestion and can last several hours. Overdose can lead to an extreme psychotic break that can result in long-term mental health problems including panic attacks, anxiety and mood disorders.

DMT (5-MeO-DMT, referred to as DMT for short, derivative of N,N-Dimethyltryptamine, hallucinogen, smoked, injected, oral administration, also known as The Business Man's Trip), is a naturally occurring neurotransmitter and tryptamine molecule that appears in the pineal gland of mammals and is found in many plants, including those used in Amazonian rituals. It can be part of a plant concoction used in many cultures for spiritual journeys and ritualistic ceremonies. It is frequently referred to as the 'spirit molecule' because of its believed connection with dreaming, near-death experiences, spiritual journeys and visionary states. 5-MeO-DMT is a methoxylated derivative of N,N DMT, first manufactured in 1936. The effects are similar to magic mushrooms and LSD but much more intense. It is produced as a white crystalline solid. When smoked, its effects last for five to 15 minutes and when orally ingested with Monoamine oxidase inhibitors (MAOIs), up to three hours. The effects, however, are so fast and so intense that the person loses control of their bodily functions and is rendered virtually unconscious, so they have to lie down. Ross, a former drug researcher for the National Institute on Drug Abuse, describes her DMT trip as highly creative with extreme time distortion, experiencing several hours within just six minutes (Reset.me, 2014).

While DMT is not addictive, its effects are so intense that it can be life-changing for many people and their personalities can change after use. Sledge & Grim (2013) reported in *The Huffington Post* that global surveys suggested an increase in international use of this drug.

W18 (4-chloro-N-[(2Z)-1-[2-(4-nitrophenyl)ethyl]piperidin-2-ylidene]benzene-1-sulfonamide) is a compound in a series of 32 substances (W1 – W32) that was initially classified as a synthetic opioid but there are now doubts about that classification. Designed as a painkiller, it was developed in Canada and patented in the US and Canada in 1984, but because of its extreme strength, supposedly 100 times stronger than fentanyl and 10,000 times stronger than heroin, no drug company would pick it up and manufacture it. Chinese illicit drug manufacturers then got hold of the formula and launched it on the illegal drug market. Kittler (2016) reports in the *Sydney Morning Herald* that since 2015 W18 has begun to appear in the US, Australia and Canada, sometimes sent by post, and in many places may not be on the controlled drug register. Since it is so strong and compact, it is easy to transport, so many drug dealers, particularly heroin dealers, have been mixing it with their drugs. This has led to many drug abusers dying from an overdose through not having known what they had bought.

Psychonauts

These are two kinds of substance users. The first are people who are experimenting with substances in an effort to explore their own mind. They often use psychedelics to this end and may take those drugs for years, considering themselves adventurers of the unconscious mind or spiritual realms that they access through those substances. A problem arises in that the person may become psychotic and unaware of their mental state.

The second kind of psychonauts are people who experiment with chemical substances that are untested and undocumented but reported to cause mind-altering experiences. In other words, they have no idea what they are about to take or the effects it may produce. They may buy these possibly legal substances on the street or via the internet. The problem is that those unknown substances can cause catastrophic effects. These substances may lead to hospitalisation, Parkinson's-like symptoms, brain damage and motor neuron disorders.

Complications

Mixing different drugs or adding alcohol is common for recreational drug users. Rarely do users take just one substance. They may take one substance to increase or change the effect of others or one substance to counteract the effects of earlier substances. The complications of multiple substance use are unpredictable and may be specific to the individual. Multiple use of substances, which one person may be able to tolerate, could kill or permanently damage another, even in the smallest amounts.

Substance use affects people vastly differently. One person may use a substance for years and have minimal side effects, yet another may die on the first dose through complications. Here I am talking about cultural plant-based drugs, manufactured recreational drugs and prescription medications.

One of the major reasons that recreational drugs have now become so popular in the world is that as production has increased, the price has diminished, making the drugs available to the poorest communities. In fact, some of the worst drug problems are in poor communities where people with few social opportunities feel their life options are limited and that drugs or alcohol are a cheap way to feel good. In a world where the media flaunts wealthy lifestyles in the face of those who do not have nor believe they could ever have wealth, more and more people are trying drugs recreationally.

Anderson, E. F. (1996). *Peyote: The divine cactus* (2nd ed.). Tucson: University of Arizona Press.

Antai-Otong, D. J. (2006). Medical complications of cocaine addiction: Clinical implications for nursing practice. *Journal of Addictions Nursing, 17*(4), 215–255. doi:10.1080/10884600600995317

Barr, A. M., Panenka, W. J., MacEwan, G. W., Thornton, A. E., Lang, D. J., Honer, W. G., & Lecomte, T. (2006). The need for speed: An update on methamphetamine addiction. *Journal of Psychiatry & Neuroscience, 31*(5), 301–313.

Bender, L., Goldschmidt, L., Sankar, D. V. S., & Freedman, A. M. (1968). Treatment of autistic schizophrenic children with LSD-25 and UML-491. In J. Wortis (Ed.), *Recent advances of biological psychiatry*. New York, NY: Springer.

Bev, T., & Patel, A. (2007). Phencyclidine intoxication and adverse effects: a clinical and pharmacological review of an illicit drug. *The California Journal of Emergency Medicine, 8*(1), 9–14.

Bone, K., & Mills, S. (2013). *Principles and practice of phytotherapy: Modern herbal medicine* (2nd ed.). London, United Kingdom: Churchill Livingstone.

Braswell, S. (2006). *American meth: A history of methamphetamine epidemic in America*. New York, NY: iUniverse.

Buss, G. D. (2006). *Morphine*. New York, NY: Chelsea House.

Campbell, C. (2016, August 17). Petrol sniffing rates in Indigenous communities fall by 88pc over 10 years, study finds. *ABC Australia*. Retrieved from http://www.abc.net.au/

Collin, M. (2010). *Altered state: The story of ecstasy culture and acid house.* London, United Kingdom: Serpent's Tail.

Conely, M. (2010, December 9). Nutmeg treated as drug for hallucinogenic high. *ABC News.* Retrieved from http://abcnews.go.com/

Cooper, R., Newton, P., & Reed, M. (1985). Neurophysiological signs of brain damage due to glue sniffing. *Electroencephalography and Clinical Neurophysiology, 60*(1), 23–26. doi:10.1016/0013-4694(85)90945-9

Discovery Channel. (2014). *Drugs, inc: Heroin: The drug devil* [YouTube video]. Available from https://www.youtube.com/watch?v=LkpUz8UHm5c

dos Santos, R. G. (Ed.). (2011). *The enthnopharmacology of ayahuasca.* Kerala, India: Transworld Research Network.

Drug 'n-bomb' that caused GC overdoses was the same drug that killed backpacker Rye Hunt. (2016, October 21). Retrieved from http://www.news.com.au/

Ferrara, S., Tedeschi, L., Frison, G., & Rossi, A. (1995). Fatality due to Gamma-Hydroxybutyric Acid (GHB) and heroin intoxication. *Journal of Forensic Sciences, 40*(3), 501-504. doi: 10.1520/JFS13816J.

Fine, D. (2014). *Hemp bound: Dispatches from the front lines of the next agricultural revolution.* White River Junction, VT: Chelsea Green.

Fletcher, B. (Director). (2011). Cannabis [Television series episode]. In S. Carter (Executive producer), *How Drugs Work.* London, United Kingdom: BBC Three.

Fletcher, B. (Director). (2011). Cocaine [Television series episode]. In S. Carter (Executive producer), *How Drugs Work.* London, United Kingdom: BBC Three.

Fletcher, B. (Director). (2011). Ecstasy [Television series episode]. In S. Carter (Executive producer), *How Drugs Work*. London, United Kingdom: BBC Three.

Fratie, P., Busardo, F. P., Cipolloni, L., De Dominicis, E., & Fineschi, V. (2015). Anabolic Androgenic Steroid (AAS) related deaths: autoptic, histopathological and toxicological findings. *Current Neuropharmacology, 13*(1), 146–159. doi: 10.2174/1570159X13666141210225414

Glatter, R. (2015). Flakka: the new designer drug you need to know about. *Forbes*. Retrieved from https://www.forbes.com/

Graybiel, A., Cramer, D. B., & Wood, C. D. (1982). Antimotion-sickness efficacy of scopolamine 12 and 72 hours after transdermal administration. *Aviation, Space, and Environmental Medicine, 53*(8), 770–772.

Hewes, J. (Executive producer). (2014). Heroin. [Television series episode]. In *Drugs, Inc.* London, United Kingdom: Wall to Wall Television.

Hofmann, A. (2009). *LSD my problem child: Reflections on sacred drugs, mysticism, and science* (4th ed.). Sarasota, FL: Multidisciplinary Association for Psychedelic Studies.

Jauregui, A. (2014, October 14). Krokodil cases being investigated: DEA 'very concerned' over reports of flesh-eating drug. *The Huffington Post*. Retrieved from http://www.huffingtonpost.com/

Kalant, H. (2001). The pharmacology and toxicology of "ecstasy" (MDMA) and related drugs. *Canadian Medical Association Journal, 165*(7), 917–928.

Khakpai, F., Nasehi, M., Haeri-Rohani, A., Eidi, A., & Zarrindast, M. R. (2012). Scopolamine induced memory impairment; Possible involvement of NMDA receptor mechanisms of dorsal hippocampus and/or septum. *Behavioural Brain Research, 231*(1), 1–10. doi:10.1016/j.bbr.2012.02.049

Kittler, K. (2016, April 29). W-18: The new street drug that is 10,000 times more toxic than morphine. *Sydney Morning Herald*. Retrieved from http://www.smh.com.au/

Kuhn, C., Swartzwelder, S., & Wilson, W. (2014). *Buzzed: The straight facts about the most used and abused drugs from alcohol to ecstasy* (4th ed.). New York, NY: W. W. Norton.

Legal highs trade has slowed to a trickle. (2016, July 21). Retrieved from http://guernseypress.com

Loeffler, J. (Producer), & Yates, E. (Director). (2006). *Crystal meth—The world's most dangerous drugs* [YouTube video]. Available from www.youtube.com

Lofft, C. (Producer). (2015). *Anabolic steroids in sports and bodybuilding* [YouTube video]. Available from https://www.youtube.com/watch?v=jQfAbcQdlng

McDaniel, C. H., & Miotto, K. A. (2001). Gamma hydroxybutyrate (GHB) and gamma butyrolactone (GBL) withdrawal: Five case studies. *Journal of Psychoactive Drugs, 33*(2), 143–149. doi:10.1080/02791072.2001.10400479

Metzner, R. (2005). *Sacred vine of spirits: Ayahuasca*. Rochester, VT: Park Street Press.

Morris, H., & Wallach, J. (2014). From PCP to MXE: A comprehensive review of the non-medical use of dissociative drugs. *Drug Testing and Analysis, 6*(7-8), 614–632. doi:10.1002/dta.162

Nestler, E. J. (2005). The neurobiology of cocaine addiction. *Science & Practice Perspectives, 3*(1), 4–10. doi:10.1151/spp05314

Olive, M. F. (2007). *Peyote and mescaline (Drugs: The straight facts)*. New York, NY: Chelsea House.

Peatfield, R., & Villilón, C. M. (2013). Headache after exposure to 'date-rape' drugs. *SpringPlus, 2*(39). doi:10.1186/2193-1801-2-39

Potash, M. N., Gordon, K. A., & Conrad, K. L. (2009). Persistent psychosis and medical complications after a single ingestion of MDMA "ecstasy"—A case report and review of the literature. *Psychiatry, 6*(7), 40–44.

Psychederic. (2015). *Swim's psychedelic cook book: Mescaline, DMT and harmalas.* (n.p.): Author.

Ratsch, C. (2005). *The encyclopedia of psychoactive plants: Ethnopharmacology and its applications.* Rochester, VT: Park Street Press.

Reset.me. (2014, June 15). *Neuroscientist describes her DMT trip* [video file]. Retrieved from https://youtu.be/yqtvuzcL84M

Rose, D. (2009, May 22). Kava can help treat anxiety. *The Sydney Morning Herald.* Retrieved from http://www.smh.com.au/

RT Documentary. (2015). *Afghan overdose: Inside opium trade* [YouTube video]. Available from https://www.youtube.com/watch?v=6psfGxfc4lg

Sahelian, R. (1998). *Kava: The miracle antianxiety herb.* New York, NY: Saint Martin's Press.

Samuel, H. (2015, September 1). Three arrested in Paris over 'devil's breath' drug that turns victims into willing 'zombies.' *The Telegraph.* Retrieved from http://www.telegraph.co.uk/

Scaccia, A. (2016, August 19). Florida zombie drug flakka: Everything you need to know. *Rolling Stone.* Retrieved from http://www.rollingstone.com/

Sim, D. (2016, September 13). Shocking photos of the crystal meth epidemic sweeping South East Asia. *International Business Times.* Retrieved from http://www.ibtimes.co.uk

Sledge, C., & Grim, R. (2013, December 10). If you haven't heard of DMT yet, you might soon. *Huffington Post*. Retrieved from http://www.huffingtonpost.com.au

Stafford, P. (1993). *Psychedelics encyclopedia* (3rd ed.). Berkeley, CA: Ronin.

Stamets, P. (1996). *Psilocybin mushrooms of the world: An identification guide*. Berkeley, CA: Ten Speed Press.

Strassman, R. J. (1984). Adverse reactions to psychedelic drugs. A review of the literature. *Journal of Nervous & Mental Disease, 172*(10), 577–595.

Sun, W.[William Sun]. (2015, December 9). *Opium in China* [Video file]. Retrieved from https://www.youtube.com/watch?v=QuOrb7_wFv0

United Nations Office on Drugs and Crime. (2008). *World drug report*. Retrieved from https://www.unodc.org/documents/wdr/WDR_2008/WDR_2008_eng_web.pdf

Velez, R. (Producer), & Evison, R. (Director). (2011). *Stepping into the fire*. United States: Dark Soup Films.

Vice. (2012). *Krokodil: Russia's deadliest drug* [YouTube video]. Available from https://www.youtube.com/watch?v=JsUH8llvTZo

Warner-Smith, M., Darke, S., Linskey, M., & Hall W. (2001). Heroin overdose: Causes and consequences. *Addiction, 96*(8), 1113–1125. doi:10.1046/j.1360-0443.2001.96811135.x

3   *Prescription Drug Abuse and Alcohol*

When the average person thinks about drug abuse, they generally only think about street drugs. They may never have any contact with such drugs or know very much about them, and this also applies to many clinicians and health workers. The truth, however, is that most drug addiction involves the prescription of legal drugs dispensed by health professionals every day.

In considering addiction of prescribed drugs it is important to think about the training of allopathic medical professionals who prescribe those drugs. There are two options generally open to allopathic medical practitioners to remedy a patient's problems: the prescription of drugs, or surgery. These professionals are not generally trained in sociology, psychotherapy or creating health, because the discipline is based on pathology. So if all you have as a practitioner is a nail and a screw, everything has to be nailed or screwed.

It is also important to consider that the majority of people drink very little alcohol. Perhaps they may have a religion that prohibits them from imbibing alcohol, maybe they are pregnant, on medication, a teetotaller, alcohol does not agree with them, they cannot afford to spend money on alcohol, or just do not see its consumption as relevant to their life.

On the other hand, it is legal in most of the world to bombard people with the concept that not only is drinking alcohol normal, but also drinking large amounts of alcohol is normal. So those who experience alcohol abuse become part of the brainwashed, targeted advertising trance, induced by manufacturers, advertisers and retailers, that it is normal to abuse alcohol. Many medical professionals do not address the dangers of alcohol, finding it a socially sensitive subject, but simply prescribe drugs to try and combat alcohol problems.

Below is a list of some of the common prescription drugs that often result in addiction.

Stimulants

Ritalin (methylphenidate, oral administration or injected) is a central nervous system stimulant used in the treatment of Attention Deficit Hyperactivity Disorder (ADHD) and in narcolepsy, for children aged six and above as well as adults. Dr Nora Volker, head of Brookhaven's Biology and Medical Departments and a neuroscientist from the National Institute on Drug Abuse in the US, theorises that for those children with ADHD and a lack of ability to concentrate and follow commands, there is little dopamine in the brain, as the brain has too many molecules that clear the dopamine away from the area where it needs to act. Ritalin prevents these proteins from clearing the dopamine away, allowing it to do its work (Wang et al., 2013). Ritalin blocks those molecules, allowing free-floating dopamine which is a neuromodulator. Volker also posited that 12 months' administration of Ritalin increased striatal dopamine transporter availability in patients diagnosed with ADHD. Once the commencement of the medication is started, the person becomes addicted to its stimulant properties. Many other medications too numerous to mention come under this bracket of stimulants. These drugs are traded in the playground in schools, particularly at exam times, when students try to perform better.

The ADHD diagnosis is highly contentious and very much a product of the American society and educational system. Opponents of the diagnosis believe that we are attempting to push our children into categorised boxes, forcing them to comply with academic stereotypes and take drugs. America has among the highest number of guns, prisoners, murders, as well as diagnosed cases of ADHD and highest administration of these medications, particularly in children. Many US schools also have security guards. The *Finland Phenomenon* documentary (Compton & Faust, 2011) shows how America has one of the Western world's worst academic school records while Finland has the highest. Finnish children spend less time at school and the country is closing its prisons and turning them into apartments. Diagnosis of ADHD in America runs at 5% (50 per thousand) of children and one per thousand in Finland.

The complications of these medications include high blood pressure, dry mouth, stomach pain, nausea, vomiting, loss of appetite, weight loss, headaches, dizziness, tingling, numbness, cold extremities, mood swings, anxiety, insomnia, sleep apnoea and other sleep problems, and dependency on the medication. What is also important to remember is that stimulants can be responsible for arrhythmia, heart attacks, delusional behaviour, hallucinations, schizoid-type behaviours, psychopathic behaviours, bipolar disorder, depression, obsessive compulsive disorder, delirium, depersonalisation and derealisation. Indeed, the *American Psychiatric Association's Diagnostic and Statistical Manual of Mental Disorders*, 5th ed. (*DSM-5*) lists 11 stimulant-related forms of psychosis (American Psychiatric Association, 2013).

Dexedrine (dextroamphetamine, oral and anal administration or injected) is prescribed for ADHD and narcolepsy. It has a long history of being one of the stimulants that was prescribed to pilots and soldiers in the Second World War as a battle performance enhancer. It has a history of having been prescribed as a dieting medication to suppress appetite and has freely been traded on the streets as a party drug. Williams, Goodale, Shay-Fiddler, Glister, & Chang (2004) examined the regular abuse of dextroamphetamine in adolescents. It carries all the usual complications and side effects of stimulants, and regular use inevitably leads to addiction with withdrawal side effects of panic attacks, anxiety, depression, mood disorders, agoraphobia and paranoia. There is a list of similar drugs in this category that are too numerous to mention.

Opioids
I have covered pain relief opioids that are used on prescription and also traded on the street illegally, such as heroin and opium, in chapter two.

Methadone hydrochloride (Dolophine and other brand names, depressant, hallucinogenic, oral administration or injected) is one of the major drugs and synthetic opioids used in opioid withdrawal therapy, mainly heroin withdrawal. It is used to reduce pain, nausea, vomiting and flu-like symptoms when addicts are in withdrawal. In some countries doctors or nurse practitioners must have special licences to prescribe its use. Its effects kick in very quickly but it can take up to four to five days for the full effect to happen. According to the World Health Organization (2008), methadone was developed in Germany in the 1930s and is commonly used throughout the world as a substitution therapy.

Administration of the drug to wean people off heroin is meant to be used at doses of 20mg to more than 100mg, over a period of four weeks to three months. Its effects are similar to other opioids in that it releases dopamine in the brain and stops the body from going deeply into withdrawal symptoms. It is administered at in-patient rehabilitation facilities, accessed as a daily direct singular dosage at pharmacies and is even dealt on the street as an illegal drug. The American Food and Drug Administration (FDA) specifically warns that its long-term use will lead to addiction (US Food & Drug Administration, 2013).

Methadone usage is hugely controversial because in the drug withdrawal industry doctors who prescribe it can have very profitable clinics, often collecting several fees per hour just for writing prescriptions. Iain Duncan-Smith, the British Member of Parliament, commented that problems arise when addicts stay on methadone for years and even decades, encouraged by their health professionals who see this as an alternative to buying heroin on the street (Holehouse, 2014). This simply causes many addicts to transfer their addictive dependency to another drug and they may never become clean and sober or integrate back into society by recovering from addiction itself.

When we look at who profits from methadone administration, we can see that what is happening is the transfer of profits from the illegal opioid drug trade to doctors and nurse practitioners, the pharmaceutical industry and dispensing chemists. Medication dispensers with few skills in actually getting addicts off all addictive substances keep addicts on methadone, not only because they do not know what else to do, but because it is profitable for their industry. Heroin addicts are literally parked on methadone, at a cost of around $5000 USD per year, rather than helped to recover from addiction. Governments give continuous money to those programs and the addicts frequently do not recover from addiction. Many doctors and chemists have been found in breach of ethics practice and even prosecuted for over-prescribing and administering methadone. The *Journal of Public Health Policy*, as far back as 2000, reported how many nations had become over-prescribers of drugs such as methadone in order to stem the spread of HIV contamination through addicts sharing needles (Fischer, 2000).

The added behavioural complications that occur with using methadone as an opioid withdrawal substitution therapy is that the patients may well, and often do, then become a multiple drug user while on the methadone. They may still take heroin, diazepams, and other drugs, while on the methadone, sometimes all in an injected cocktail. As Russell Brand, the British comedian and recovered drug addict, pointed out in his documentary *From Addiction to Recovery* (Anthony, Hartford, Moore, & Wilson, 2012), addicts do not tell doctors that they are abusing the methadone by using it as a free drug to add to their cock-tail of drugs, and many doctors do not want to know the whole story. The addict has not ceased to be an addict, they have simply become an addict of another kind. It becomes a trance of con-tinuous addiction shared by all in the circle.

The painkiller epidemic

In the documentary *Pill Overkill: America's Pain Killer Epidemic* (Davies, Sharkey, Tozer, & Weitenberg, 2015), we see this is an addictive phenomenon that is particularly prevalent in America, with Staten Island being one of the leading places. However, this phenomenon exists in many other states and countries and particularly Australia. Doctors across the globe are prescrib-ing opioid-based painkillers such as oxycodone, codeine (only available in generic form), fentanyl (Actiq, Duragesic, Fentora), hydrocodone (Hysingla ER, Zohydro ER), hydrocodone/acet-aminophen (Lorcet, Lortab, Norco, Vicodin), hydromorphone (Dilaudid, Exalgo), meperidine (Demerol, Pethidine) and similar drugs with different trade names. Each of these brand-name drugs may appear under different names in different parts of the world. While methadone belongs in this type of drug, I have dealt with it separately because of its usage in heroin withdrawal therapy.

In the documentary *The Oxycontin Express* (van Zeller, 2015), we see the addiction to this drug being fuelled by doctors acting as legalised drug dealers in Florida. Thousands of people descend on Florida every week from the surrounding states to buy drugs to take back to their state to sell. People are going into doctors' offices and coming out with supplies of hundreds of pills, going back the next week and being prescribed the same amounts. Old women are going into multiple doctors' offices in a day complaining of pain and cashing hundreds of prescriptions a month that they sell on street corners. Doctors are setting up pain management clinics, advertising free extra medication with every purchase, and making millions of dollars a year.

In Canada, the documentary *Fentanyl: The Drug Deadlier than Heroin* (VICE, 2016) shows addicts struggling to make money for their daily fentanyl, where a record number of people are dying from overdoses. Fentanyl is now being used by addicts as a replacement for oxycontin since its formula was changed and it is much stronger and more addictive. Much of this may not be obtained on prescription but is smuggled in from China since it is concentrated enough to transport in small packages and is highly profitable to drug dealers. It is swallowed, snorted, smoked or injected and is often reported by users to be even more addictive than heroin. Recovery services are reported to be unable to keep up with the escalating levels of addiction. Withdrawal from addiction can be extremely difficult with these drugs. The client experiences serious symptoms such as profound anxiety, severe panic attacks, reduction in memory and cognitive abilities, reduced social skills and difficulty holding down a job.

In Australia, the New South Wales State Coroner Michael Barnes issued a warning in 2016 about a "deadly" batch of heroin, which was believed to be cut with fentanyl (Metherell, 2016). This has been a problem in other parts of Australia such as Adelaide. Addicts scoring on the street were not really sure what they were buying, which led to a spate of deaths by overdose. The University of New South Wales found that up to 70% of all opioid deaths were due to opioid painkillers such as fentanyl and others (Roxburgh & Breen, 2016). Regardless of the country's accurate prescribing records, the drug was being brought in from China and sold on the streets.

Anti-depressants

As a society we have been sold the idea of the magic pill: a pill for this, that and the other. It is part of the instant gratification marketing ploy that is propagated by a commercialised society and consumerism. Pharmaceutical companies and medics are trying to sell a pill to counteract every aspect of human experience.

Depression has been classified as a mental illness, diagnosed mainly by GPs in five minutes flat with virtually no real information about the patient's life, and the sale of a pill has been made. The number of anti-depressant items prescribed and dispensed in England more than doubled between 2005 and 2015 (Prescribing and Medicines Team Health and Social Care Information Centre, 2016). Pratt, Brody, & Qiuping (2011) noted that 11% of North Americans aged 12 and above took anti-depressant medications. Of those, less than one-third taking one anti-depressant medication and less than one-half of those taking multiple anti-depressants had seen a mental health professional the previous year.

Human beings are meant to experience depression during certain times of their lives. In my book *Inspiration for Survive and Prosper* (O'Keefe, 2013), I talk about how those depression or traumatic periods are points of demarcation in our lives that are telling us to change direction and do something different. This is not, for most people, mental illness but our bodies and minds telling us we must adapt and change. Depression, or melancholia as it was once called, is a natural emotion and process that as human beings we must work through to rehabilitate ourselves in order to feel better again.

The *British Medical Journal* published a meta-analysis by researchers led by Danube University that reviewed 11 studies showing anti-depressants were no more effective than counselling, including cognitive behavioural therapy, for mild to severe depression (Amick et al., 2015). The publication came after prescribing of anti-depressants in recent years in the UK were escalating, with one in 10 people asking for prescriptions. In looking at this study, we must also consider that if the results were equal to therapy, the placebo effect would also account for some of the medication figures, which potentially makes anti-depressants less effective than counselling.

Ferguson, back in 2001, clearly identified the possible side effects of anti-depressants, which are well documented, including increasing nausea, depression, anxiety, foggy mind, impotence, lowered sexual desire, insomnia, skin rash, muscle pains, reduced blood clotting factor, diarrhoea, suicidal thoughts, muscle spasms, tics, dyskinesia (repetitive muscle spasms), Parkinson-ism-like symptoms, loss of fine motor control and restlessness, which are more likely in the elderly (Ferguson, 2001). Clinicians, however, rarely warn patients of possible side effects of medications because they do not have the time. They also fear the patients will not take the medication.

A Harvard Medical School publication warns that anti-depressants can cross the placental barrier in pregnant women, affecting the foetus, and that the drugs may become ineffective after a few months or years (Harvard Health Publications, 2014).

In her book *The Pill That Steals Lives*, the documentary maker Katinka Newman described how anti-depressant medication made her become profoundly psychotic with violent hallucinations, resulting in a decline in mental health over the next few years (Newman, 2016). She is one of many similar reported cases.

However, Edersheim, & Stern (2009) talk about how, in assessing and prescribing to patients, the test of the 'Tort law' comes into play, in that if the clinician does not prescribe some medication, they fear they may be sued for failure of duty of care. Even though the medical situation is a professional contract of duty of care, not prescribing runs the danger of legal harm being proved against the professional. What this means is that medical staff prescribe medications continually, even when their patient may be better served by other means. So let us ask: is it normal that such a large part of the population of the US is really suffering from a mental illness called depression or are the pharmaceutical companies using clever marketing?

Dr Robert Lefever, a physician writing for the *Daily Mail*, spoke about how doctors are just as addicted to giving anti-depressant medication as patients are at asking for it for problems of normal living (Lefever, 2012). There are several types of anti-depressants on the market and different people experience different effects from those drugs. The addiction to anti-depressants occurs when people are prescribed them when they do not need them but become psychologically dependent on them. It also occurs when people feel unwell when they try to come off them, which is common and called discontinuation syndrome. What tends to happen is that people stay on the anti-depressants for years, unsupervised by one specific clinician, instead tending to keep getting prescriptions from different doctors, without actually dealing with their life problems. They literally become anti-depressant junkies.

Broadhead (1994) discusses how the misdiagnosis of depression is also incredibly common amongst medical professionals. Many clinicians mistake conditions such as fibromyalgia, chronic fatigue syndrome, mitochondrial dysfunction, MTHFR gene polymorphism, adrenal collapse, hypothyroidism, hypoglycaemia, hypotension, inflammation of the gut and eating disorders as depression. Also GPs often prescribe anti-depressants for anxiety, obsessive compulsive disorders and addiction. So they prescribe anti-depressant medications for problems the patient may not have, including at times prescribing off label for an unclear diagnosis, which the patient may end up taking for years and may become addicted to.

Continuous side effects can include increasing depression, fogginess of the mind, psychosis and suicidal thoughts.

Anxiolytics, sedatives and sleeping pills
In considering these three categories of medications, they are put together because the same medications may be used for all three purposes.

As a broader umbrella they are described as calmatives, hypnotics (sleep-inducing) and tranquillisers and are intended to settle the patient down when they are anxious, distressed or unable to sleep.

Valium, temazepam, diazepam, oxazepam, nitrazepam, lorazepam, Xanax, chlordiazepoxide, clonazepam (oral administration or injected) and a whole host of generics (benzodiazepines) are used as muscle relaxants, anti-convulsants, anti-seizures medication, anxiolytics, anti-psychotics and hypnotics. In many cases they are meant as a short-term treatment but in some psychiatric cases and in cases of physical convulsions, pain and intensive care, they may be used long term. They induce drowsiness, reduction in cognitive abilities, fogginess of the mind, lowered reaction times, reduction in motivation and a quick state of disassociation. Benzodiazepines are also dealt on the street as street drugs. In in-patient care their use is monitored but in outpatient care there is a huge risk of abuse. Brunette, Noordsy, Halyi, & Drake (2003) surveyed use and abuse in patients with severe mental illness and substance abusers. Abuse, however, is much wider in the general population, with some people having taken these drugs daily for decades.

Dosage determines how soporific the person becomes. Side effects can include addiction, suppressed breathing and associated respiratory problems, newborn dependence due to dependent mothers, increase in physical seizures or epilepsy, disinhibition, aggression and suicidal thoughts. Pétursson (1994) described benzodiazepine withdrawal experiences as including sleep disturbance, irritability, increase in tension, anxiety, panic attacks, sweating, dry retching and nausea, palpitations, headaches, muscular stiffness and perceptual changes.

Barbiturates (derived from barbituric acid, oral administration or injection) act on suppressing the central nervous system and are an older class of medication which have largely been replaced by benzodiazepines due to overdose giving rise to the risk of death. They display analgesic effects but may not be used with anaesthetics. Medications such as **phenobarbital, sodium pentothal** and **thiopental** are still used, particularly in veterinary practice. They are also still used today as anti-convulsives. Dependence and addiction is a risk noted by Harris & Fraser (1950) as far back as the 1950s, particularly in older people whose livers do not detox fast. Large doses are used in euthanasia to stop the heart.

Z drugs are a series of drugs used to induce sleep without the disturbances that people may experience with benzodiazepines. Drugs such as **Zopiclone** and **Zaleplon** are illicitly used by heroin addicts to help them get to sleep. The *Journal.ie* reported that Irish Minister Simon Harris introduced legislation in 2016 to have Z drugs classified as controlled substances due to dealing by gangs in Dublin (Hayes, 2016).

Anti-psychotics (neuroleptics, major tranquillisers, oral administration or injected) are generally used with severe psychiatric cases, such as managing psychosis, schizophrenia, hallucinations, paranoia, delusions, major depression and bipolar disorder. The first generation are known as typical anti-psychotics and the second generation are known as atypical. Both block dopamine pathways and atypicals also act on serotonin receptors. The major area of abuse with these drugs is not with the person taking the medication but with medical staff overprescribing them, which leads to addiction, including in children. Patients themselves usually dislike taking these drugs because they make them feel so dissociated from the world, along with a whole list of side effects including muscle spasms, tardive dyskinesia, dry mouth, blurred vision, depression and weight gain. Perkins (2002) observed that only around 50% of schizophrenics complied to prescribed medication protocols.

The American Psychological Society reported that many Americans are taking medications that may not be working for them due to insufficient assessment, failure to monitor results and the desire for medical staff to contain and manage patient behaviour (Smith, 2012).

Baker (2015), in *Global News*, Canada, reported that nearly one third of geriatric residents in care homes were being prescribed anti-psychotics as a mechanism to control their behaviours, which led to addiction. Once on an anti-psychotic, it is very hard to come off, even if a person has been misdiagnosed. All too common is the misdiagnosis of psychosis by psychiatrists, as Rapapport (2006) explains in relation to patients' loss of civil rights due to enforced treatment and incarceration.

Anaesthetics

Some of the abusers of these medications are anaesthesiologists themselves who can end up falsifying hospital records when they become addicted. Knaus (2015), in the *Canberra Times*, reported a case of an anaesthesiologist at the Calvary Hospital who took left-over medication after surgery for personal use. In such cases, as with this one, medical staff are usually suspended, enter an addiction recovery program and then at some later stage reinstated. This is also the case with many medical staff where they are tempted by readily available drugs and are perhaps under pressure at work or home. Berge, Seppala, & Schipper (2009) assert that between 10–12% of doctors suffer addiction at some time during their career.

Propofol (marketed as **Diprivan**, injected) was given to pop star Michael Jackson by his private physician to help him sleep, for which the physician was later found guilty of involuntary manslaughter (Medina, 2011). Anaesthetics can also be prescribed by doctors in private practice. The drug is for the initiation and maintenance of general anaesthetic, often in combination with other drugs. It is administered intravenously, causing unconsciousness within about two minutes. Its side effects include irregular heartbeat and supressed respiration. In Jackson's case its administration resulted in death as he was unable to be revived. Medical staff sometimes use micro doses of these drugs themselves to calm their nerves, and become addicted to them.

Ketamine (marketed as **Ketalar** and other names, oral administration, snorted or injected) is used in general anaesthetics and as sedation for pain relief with extreme pain. Veterinary medicine also uses this drug for sedating and stunning animals, particularly large ones, for capture; hence as a street drug it is often known as the elephant tranquilliser. It produces a trance-like state, derealisation and hallucinations, which accounts for the *New York Times* reporting its popularity as a recreational club drug referred to as Special K (Pollack, 2014). Users often describe their experience as going down the 'K hole'. While there have been experiments using this drug as an anti-depressant at Yale University (Bruce, 2015), its addictive nature may not promise much value in this regard in general medicine. The side effects of withdrawal include tachycardia, hypertension, nausea, vomiting, numbness, depression, amnesia, hallucinations and respiratory distress.

Fentanyl (oral or intravenous administration, snorted, smoked) is a synthetic opioid. I have included it in this section as well as a previous section because it has also been used as an anaesthetic (intravenously) along with other drugs and as an analgesic. This is one of the most problematic drugs because it is said to be a hundred times more addictive than heroin. Tens of thousands of people have died from overdose and complications of the drug over the past number of years. The documentary *Fentanyl: The Drug Deadlier than Heroin* (VICE, 2016) shows whole communities devastated by the spread of fentanyl.

Kinetz (2017) reports that in 2017 China added synthetic opioids including **Carfentanil** and the less potent **furanyl fentanyl**, **acryl fentanyl** and **valeryl fentanyl** under controlled drugs. These were being sent through the post by Chinese dealers to America and other countries, and heroin dealers have been cutting heroin with these drugs for greater profits but, as mentioned previously, this has led to many addicts overdosing accidentally. While China stated it wishes to take more responsibility in regards to the world's drug problems, its ability to control its illicit drug manufacturers remains to be seen.

Alcohol

Professor David Nut, a British psychiatrist and neuropsychopharmacologist, clearly stated in *The Guardian*, UK, that alcohol is a toxin, which can be shown by its ability to kill cells and micro-organisms (Nut, 2011). It is absorbed in the small intestines and, according to the World Health Organization (n.d.), in 2012 about 3.3 million net deaths, or 5.9% of all global deaths, were attributable to alcohol consumption.

The effects of alcohol on the body include light-headedness, loss of balance, loss of body heat, loss of sensory awareness, nausea, vomiting, diarrhoea, glucose dysregulation, weight gain, loss of inhibition, excitement, loss of judgement and analytical skills, reduced reaction times, reduced access to memory, created state-dependent memory, inability to multi-task, can make people want to eat more, and in some people, makes them more aggressive and violent. Some people get more intoxicated than others quicker because the concentration of alcohol in the blood determines the level of its effects. People who have more water in their body get less drunk on the same amount of alcohol and the more muscle someone has, the more water is carried in the muscles. If someone has eaten before they drink, intoxication is less effective because some of the digestion of the alcohol takes place in the stomach. Alcoholics, however, tend to drink alcohol and not eat, getting their empty calories from the alcohol, which is devoid of nutrition.

The documentary, *The Truth About Alcohol* (Abdelmoneim & Briggs, 2016), features several experts on alcohol detoxification in the liver who note that when the liver begins to detoxify, it gets rid of one unit of alcohol per hour, regardless of how much the person has drunk. So the person who has drunk a large amount of alcohol will take longer to recover. The person who drinks constantly will have a liver that is continually occupied in the process of alcohol detoxification. The older someone gets, the less the liver is able to detoxify the alcohol. While alcohol seems to help induce sleep initially, it disturbs it later into the night, reducing REM sleep particularly, which is a major indicator of deep sleep.

Just like the reach of the pharmaceutical industry into the prescribing of profit-driven drug administration, the alcohol industry also spends billions of dollars lobbying to promote its product. Martino, Miller, Coomber, Hancock, & Kypri (2017) pointed out in their research into the alcohol industry's lobbying that many of the manufacturers were placing their representatives on public health policy consultation committees on responsible drinking. Their research concluded that allowing manufacturers to be part of public health policy was not only biased but allowed leeway for profit to be put ahead of public health. They are not, after all, just a stakeholder, but a commercial enterprise seeking to increase their profits above all else.

According to the Distilled Spirit Council of the United States, "The U.S. beverage alcohol industry is a major contributor to the economy, responsible for over $400 billion in total U.S. economic activity in 2010, generating nearly $90 billion in wages and over 3.9 million jobs for U.S. workers" (Distilled Spirits Council, n.d.). Not only was alcohol one of the most profitable industries of the 20th century, but also the most widely available drug, protected by governments that took a cut of the profits through tax. The industry only partly cleans up the problems it causes and is allowed to trade legally in most parts of the world. Its promoters and advertising have stylised alcohol in the public eye as totally acceptable, desirable and fashionable in all the forms it is sold.

Sacks, Gonzales, Bouchery, Tomedi, & Brewer (2015) found that the cost to the US government for excess drinking of alcohol amounted to $249.0 billion in 2010. The cost to both the public purse and private health funds of alcohol-associated complications probably goes into the trillions of dollars per year for the US alone. Official figures of the cost of alcoholism to countries do not reflect secondary illnesses from alcohol use and abuse, as this is not entered into the public record.

We have to remember that in many countries the tax revenue from the alcohol industry is a large part of the taxation revenue, meaning that upsetting the alcohol industry is often the very last thing that politicians and governments want. In *Strange Brew: Alcohol and Government Monopoly*, Whitman looks at the deeply entrenched financial system that the American governments have with the alcohol industry and how it is designed to profit both, rather than solely protect the public health (Whitman, 2003).

The Center for Disease Control and Prevention in the US stated on its website that there were "88,000 deaths and 2.5 million years of potential life lost work days (YPLL) each year in the United States from 2006–2010" (Center for Disease Control and Prevention, 2016). To record the number of alcoholics in a society is impossible statistically. Calculations are generally arrived at by identifying those using public health systems. Many alcoholics, however, do not use public health systems, which may have limited resources and capacity to help those seeking assistance. Voluntary organisations, charities, religious organisations and self-help networks probably help the larger number of people with alcoholic problems who do not show up in government statistics, which are often gathered from lower socio-economic groups. The private health sector, where many alcoholics seek help, generally do not keep such figures, unless they are inclined to apply for government or private grants.

Knapton (2014), a senior science correspondent for the *Telegraph*, UK, reported the British government had to reverse incoming guidelines for placing minimum prices on alcohol given by the Chief Medical Officers of England, Scotland, Wales and Northern Ireland. Under pressure from the drinks industry, government ministers reversed their own recommendations in 2014, after meeting with the industry lobbies more than 130 times. This is a common scenario in every part of the world where alcohol is legal. A government cannot sufficiently warn people of health-related dangers of alcohol or excess drinking of alcohol because they are gagged by the alcohol industry.

Everyone is familiar with the sight of a drunk person and all the behavioural problems that occur when someone has lost control of their body and behaviour. What most people are not aware of, or choose to ignore, is the vast array of physical and mental problems that arise from minimal drinking. Hatchard et al. (2015) show how even minimal drinking can have effects on neurophysiological development and slow down brain growth in the young. Alcohol-related health problems come in three forms: acute, chronic and secondary.

The *Old Before My Time* alcohol documentary (Faragher, Hindey, & Williams, 2015) shows teenagers and people in their early twenties who drink to excess. Alcoholic poisoning from over-use leads to people being admitted to hospital, sometimes unconscious. This may be accompanied by organ failure, heart attack, lung deterioration, brain damage and premature ageing. Alcoholic poisoning also includes the risk of motor vehicle incidents where the driver was intoxicated and crashed. This often results in physical trauma to the driver as well as trauma or death to other people involved. At times this can include drivers who are alcoholics but also it can include drivers who simply drank over the legal limit and lost control of their vehicles.

Esper, Burnham, & Moss (2006) discussed the multifaceted pathologies due to chronic alcohol use. This can include cirrhosis of the liver and liver failure, kidney failure, brain damage, neuropathy, cardio-vascular disease, hypertension, lung failure, Cushing's Disease, obesity, pancreatitis, lymphedema, diabetes, broken bones due to accident, fractures due to deossification of the bone, metabolic dysfunction, gastrointestinal problems, malnutrition, erectile dysfunction, gynecomastia, cancer, amenorrhoea, depression, anxiety and psychosis.

Secondary effects of long-term alcohol use and abuse can include cirrhosis of the liver, kidney dysfunction, foetal alcohol syndrome, immune dysfunction, malnutrition, diabetes, hormonal dysregulation, hypertension, hypercholesterolemia, elevated homocysteine, oxidative stress, misshapen red blood cells and increased risk of cancer. All this can happen at two drinks a day and, in some people, even lower amounts.

Boileau et al. (2003) find physiologically alcohol promotes the release of dopamine in the brain, not in all of the brain but generally in the reward pathways. This could explain why people with low levels of dopamine may become more easily addicted to alcohol. It could also explain why alcoholics keep going back to alcohol to get the dopamine rush, but repeated exposure to alcohol will lower the brain's natural production of dopamine, thereby making the person reliant on alcohol.

We can see how both prescribed drugs and alcohol, while legal, can be and are dangerous hazards to health which can lead to addiction, with all the accompanying complications. Medicine is a money-making industry, not just philanthropic. Where profits are the major drivers of prescribing medications, both the pharmaceutical industry and medical staff themselves create addictions.

It is important to remember that alcohol is not a harmless recreational libation, but a deadly poison with profound detrimental effects on health. In the quest for profit and taxes, the public is not truly educated around the dangers of alcohol addiction.

Most people live in a trance, seduced by the alcohol and pharmaceutical industries' marketing material that they have imbibed all their lives. 'The doctor knows best' belief turns out to be incorrect a great deal of the time when prescribing poorly tested, under-reported, harmful and addictive medications.

'It's cool to have a drink' turns out to be the catchphrase that those unenlightened and uneducated around the dangers and side effects of alcohol on the body accept as the truth.

For anyone at any time of their lives addiction can so easily be just around the corner.

Abdelmoneim, J. (Presenter) & Briggs, D. (Director). (2016). Alcohol [Television series episode]. In S. Anthony (Executive producer), *The Truth About....* London, England: BBC One.

American Psychiatric Association. (2013). *Diagnostic and statistical manual of mental disorders* (5th ed.). Arlington, VA: Author.

Amick, H. R., Gartlehner, G., Gaynes B. N., Forneris, C., Asher G. N., Morgan, L. C., . . . Lohr, K. N. (2015). Comparative benefits and harms of second generation antidepressants and cognitive behavioral therapies in initial treatment of major depressive disorder: Systematic review and meta-analysis. *BMJ, 351.* doi:10.1136/bmj.h6019

Anthony, S., Hartford, L., Moore, C. (Producers), & Wilson, R. (2012). *Russell Brand from addiction to recovery* [Motion picture]. United Kingdom: Matchlight.

Baker, P. (2015, April 7). Antipsychotic drugs being prescribed to a third of seniors in residential care. *Global News Canada.* Retrieved from http://globalnews.ca/

Berge, K. H., Seppala, M. D., & Schipper, A. M. (2009). Chemical dependency and the physician. *Mayo Clinic Proceedings,* 284(7), 625–631. doi:10.1016/S0025-6196(11)60751-9

Boileau, I., Assaad, J. M., Pihl, R. O., Benkelfat, C., Leyton, M., Diksic M., . . . Dagher, A. (2003). Alcohol promotes dopamine release in the human nucleus accumbens. *Synapse, 49*(4), 226–31.

Broadhead, E. (1994). Misdiagnosis of depression: Physicians contribute to the stigmatization of mental illness. *Archives of Family Medicine,* 3(4), 319–320.

Bruce, L. (2015). Suicide prevention and ketamine. *Yale Research*

Program. Retrieved from: http://depression.yale.edu/

Brunette, M. F., Noordsy, D. L., Halyi, X., & Drake, R. E. (2003). Benzodiazepine use and abuse among patients with severe mental illness and co-occurring substance abuse. *Psychiatric Services, 54*(10), 1395–1401.

Center for Disease Control and Prevention. (2016). *Fact sheets – Alcohol use and your health.* Retrieved from https://www.cdc.gov/alcohol/fact-sheets/alcohol-use.htm

Compton, R. A. (Producer), & Faust, S. (Director). (2011). *The Finland phenomenon* [Motion picture]. United States: New School Films.

Davies, G., Sharkey, R., Tozer, J., & Weitenberg, C. (Producers). (2015). Pill overkill: America's painkiller epidemic [Television series episode]. In B. Lim (Executive producer), *Dateline.* Artarmon, Australia: SBS One.

Distilled Spirits Council. (n.d.). Economic contributions of the distilled spirits industry. Retrieved from http://www.discus.org/economics/

Edersheim, J.G., & Stern, T. A. (2009). Liability associated with prescribing medications. *Primary Care Companion to the Journal of Clinical Psychiatry, 11*(3), 115–119.

Esper, A., Burnham, E. L., & Moss, M. (2006). The effect of alcohol abuse on ARDS and multiple organ dysfunction. *Minerva Anestesiologica, 72*(6), 375–81.

Ferguson, J. M. (2001). SSRI antidepressant medications: Adverse effects and tolerability. *Primary Care Companion to the Journal of Clinical Psychiatry, 3*(1), 22–27.

Fischer, B. (2000). Prescriptions, power and politics: The turbulent history of methadone maintenance in Canada. *Journal of Public Health Policy, 21*(2), 187–210.

Harris, I., & Fraser, H. F. (1950). Addiction to analgesics and barbiturates. *Pharmacological Reviews, 2*(2), 335–397.

Harvard Health Publications. (2014, March). *What are the real risks of antidepressants?* Retrieved from http://www.health.harvard.edu

Hatchard, T., Smith, A. M., Halchuk, R. E., Longo, C. A., Fried, P. A., Hogan, M. J., & Cameron, I. (2015). Effects of low-level alcohol use on cognitive interference: An fMRI study in young adults. *Alcohol, 49*(1), 7–13. doi:10.1016/j.alcohol.2014.07.020.

Hayes, I. (2016, June 23). Health Minister moves to make 'Z-drugs' a controlled substance in wake of gangland murders. *The Journal.ie.* Retrieved from http://www.thejournal.ie/

Healey, C. (Presenter) & Williams, T. (Director). (2015). Alcohol [Television series episode]. In C. Faragher & E. Hindey (Executive producers), *Old Before My Time.* London, England: BBC Three.

Holehouse, M. (2014). Now fight the methadone industry that keeps addicts hooked, says Iain Duncan Smith. *The Telegraph.* Retrieved from http://www.telegraph.co.uk

Kinetz, E. (2017, February 16). China's ban of a deadly tranquilizer could be a 'game changer' in North America's opioid epidemic. *U. S. News & World Report.* Retrieved from https://www.usnews.com/

Knapton, S. (2014, January 7). Were ministers under the influence of drinks industry? *The Telegraph.* Retrieved from http://www.telegraph.co.uk/

Knaus, C. (2015, January 27). Doctor took leftover anaesthetic for personal use: Tribunal. *The Canberra Times.* Retrieved from http://www.canberratimes.com.au/

Lefever, R. (2012, June 8). Anti-depressants are merely another addiction – for doctors as well as the patients. *Daily Mail UK*. Retrieved from http://www.dailymail.co.uk/

Martino F. P., Miller, P. G., Coomber, K., Hancock, L., & Kypri, K. (2017). Analysis of alcohol industry submissions against marketing regulation. *PLoS One*, *12*(4). doi:10.1371/journal.pone.0170366

Medina, J. (2011, November 7). Doctor is guilty in Michael Jackson's death. *The New York Times*. Retrieved from https://www.nytimes.com/

Metherell, L. (2016, June 7). Fentanyl: Spate of fatal overdoses in Sydney could be linked to drug blamed for Prince's death. *ABC News Australia*. Retrieved from http://www.abc.net.au/news/

Newman, K. B. (2016). *The pill that steals lives: One woman's terrifying journey to discover the truth about antidepressants*. London, UK: John Blake.

Nut, D. (2011, March 7). There is no such thing as a safe level of alcohol consumption. *The Guardian*. Retrieved from https://www.theguardian.com/

O'Keefe, T. (2013). *Inspiration for survive and prosper: Personal Transformation Out of Crisis*. Fremantle, Australia: Vivid.

Perkins, D. O. (2002) Predictors of noncompliance in patients with schizophrenia. *The Journal of Clinical Psychiatry*, *63*(12), 1121–1128. doi:10.4088/JCP.v63n1206

Pétursson, H. (1994). The benzodiazepine withdrawal syndrome. *Addiction, 89,* 1455–1459.

Pollack, A. (2014, December 9). Special K, a hallucinogen, raises hopes and concerns as a treatment for depression. *The New*

York Times. Retrieved from https://www.nytimes.com/

Pratt, L., Brody, D., & Qiuping, G. (2011, October). *Antidepressant use in persons aged 12 and over: United States, 2005–2008.* Retrieved from https://www.cdc.gov/nchs/data/databriefs/db76.htm

Prescribing and Medicines Team Health and Social Care Information Centre. (2016). *Prescriptions dispensed in the community 2005-2015.* Leeds, UK: Health and Social Care Information Centre

Rapapport, R. G. (2006). Losing your rights: Complications of misdiagnosis. *Journal of the American Academy of Psychiatry and the Law, 34*(4), 436–438.

Roxburgh, A., and Breen, C. (2016). *Accidental drug-induced deaths due to opioids in Australia,* 2012. Sydney: National Drug and Alcohol Research Centre, UNSW

Sacks J. J., Gonzales, K. R., Bouchery, E. E., Tomedi, L. E., & Brewer, R. D. (2015). 2010 national and state costs of excessive alcohol consumption. *American Journal of Preventative Medicine, 49*(5), e73–e79. doi:10.1016/j.amepre.2015.05.031

Smith, B. L. (2012). Inappropriate prescribing. *Monitor on Psychology, 43*(6), 34.

U. S. Food & Drug Administration. (2013). *Information for healthcare professionals methadone hydrochloride.* Retrieved from https://www.fda.gov/Drugs/DrugSafety/PostmarketDrugSafetyInformationforPatientsandProviders/ucm142841.htm

van Zeller, M. (Correspondent). (2015). The oxycontin express [Television series episode]. In M. Koss & A. Yamaguchi (Executive producers), *Vanguard.* San Francisco, CA: Current TV.

VICE (2016, July 22). *Fentanyl: The drug deadlier than heroin*

[Video file]. Retrieved from https://www.youtube.com/
watch?v=28rJqj-7pEY

Wang, G.-J., Volkow, N. D., Wigal, T., Kollins, S. H., Newcorn, J.
F., Telang, F., . . . Swanson, J. M. (2013). Long-term stimulant treatment affects brain dopamine transporter level in
patients with attention deficit hyperactive disorder. *PLoS
One, 8*(5). doi:10.1371/journal.pone.0063023

Whitman, D. G. (2003). *Strange brew: Alcohol and government
monopoly.* Oakland, CA: The Independent Institute.

Williams, R. J., Goodale, L. A., Shay-Fiddler, M. A., Glister, B.
N., & Chang, S. Y. (2004). Methylphenidate and dextro-
amphetamine abuse in substance-abusing adolescence.
The American Journal of Addiction, 13(4), 381–389.

World Health Organization. (2008). The methadone fix. *Bulletin of the World Health Organization, 86*(3), 164–165.
Retrieved from http://www.who.int/bulletin/en/

World Health Organization. (n.d.). Retrieved from
http://www.who.int

4 Stop Drugs and Alcohol Hypnotherapy

Pre-hypnosis

It took me 20 years to build the 6-Step Stop Drugs and Alcohol Clinical Hypnotherapy Model. I reviewed the notes and cases of thousands of clients I had seen to stop drugs and alcohol. That review included the cases that were great successes, the ones that were not and what went wrong, or where there were missing elements from treatment. Over time, patterns began to emerge around the cases that were successful and stages the recovering addict and myself, as a therapist, went through.

One of the most important things I noted was that people recovering from addiction needed structure. When an addict has no structure, their body is not in a state of homeostasis, the mind is in disarray, and their personal life and social circumstances may have deteriorated, in the worst case, to the point of no return. Their employment history becomes chequered and scattered and if they are in business, they cease to pay good attention to their affairs.

What is equally as important is that as a therapist I had to have structure in the way I guided people to sobriety. While I can have empathy with their circumstances, I could never enter into the chaos of the addict's world. The therapist must always be objective and guide the client, even when the client thinks they are guiding the therapist.

What is addiction?

As clinicians dealing with drug and alcohol addictions, we

can look closely at what addiction might be and the answer depends on who is asking the question. The answer, of course, may at times be hotly contested and may change according to many perspectives.

Legally addiction is generally associated with the taking of and dependency on substances that might be illegal or produce legally unacceptable behaviour brought on by legal substances. The drunk in the street causing a nuisance may be charged with public order offences but not with possession of alcohol. The heroin addict passed out on the street who has the drug on them may also be charged with a public disorder offence, as well as possession of an illegal substance. The differentiation also depends on the country, its laws, whether the police are busy that night or whether police corruption and misconduct is involved. Bowling & Phillips (2007) reported in *The Modern Law Review Limited* that in the UK darker-skinned people were more likely to be stopped and searched than Caucasian people. Similar studies have shown parallels in the US, so in predominantly Caucasian-based societies, darker-skinned people are more likely to be labelled drug offenders.

The *International Classification of Diseases* (1CD 10) classifies substance use and physical addiction under mental and behavioural disorders (World Health Organization, 2011). The fact that a drug may cause withdrawal symptoms is not necessarily a sign of addiction as LSD, for instance, can give rise to withdrawal symptoms but people do not necessarily become addicted to it, even though they may become regular users. However, the need to take the substance in order to retain any sense of physical or mental well-being is a sign of addiction. When the person senses they need the drug to restore or maintain well-being to avoid vomiting, anxiety, depression, panic attacks or profuse sweating, they may indeed be experiencing signs of physical addiction.

The *Diagnostic and Statistical Manual of Mental Disorders Manual (DSM-5)* classifies addiction under substance use disorders (American Psychiatric Association, 2013). Mental addiction is as much a driver to take or abuse a substance as physical addiction. People may feel emotionally that they have to take cocaine to socialise with their friends, take heroin for fear of physical withdrawal symptoms, continue with slimming pills to avoid putting on weight, or take anti-depressants or sleeping pills because the doctor told them they should. The compulsion to abuse a substance can clearly be present without the presence of physical addiction.

Social addiction can be looked at from the perspective of organisational and social compliance theory in psychology, in that groups of two or more people behave in ways that comply to the perceived or actual social norm. Vaughan & Hogg (2014) review the perfect example of this with the infamous Stanford Prison experiment, headed by Zimbardo, when participants in a behavioural experiment, who were asked to behave as guards, adopted cruel and aggressive behaviours. In cultures and sub-cultures where substance use is the norm, individual addiction may be less obvious, but in cultures where substance use is abnormal, addiction can be more obvious and less socially acceptable. Social compliance theory also teaches us that individuals behave in abnormal ways to conform to social norms and guidelines, so substance users follow other substance users into substance abuse and patients generally comply with the instructions given by medical authority figures, often without question.

Once the addiction has started, many people believe they are powerless to stop their perceived need for the substances they abuse, even to the point of putting their own lives and the lives of others in danger to be able to use the substance. Reason, logic, moral code and rationale can all become out of the reach of the addict's mental state, not necessarily through conscious choice, but because normal rational, mental functioning is suspended. The addict is locked into an altered state of repetitious thoughts and behaviours, fuelled by their addiction.

In working with addicts, hypnotherapists need to ascertain the drivers of the clients' legal, social, physical and mental addiction to understand what drives the addiction. Observation and information sourcing informs the therapist on what strategies they need to use with the client to stop the addiction and the leverage available to create single, double and triple binds in their hypnotic communications.

Why clean and sober?

The model I teach is a clean and sober, total abstinence model. If someone has had substance abuse issues, unless they are clean and sober, at some stage they are likely to drift back into addiction. I have seen this time and time again, not only in the therapy room but also in life. The clean and sober model is not new as it is used by Alcoholics Anonymous, Narcotics Anonymous and many other organisations involved in addiction recovery (Alcoholics Anonymous World Services Inc, 2001). Heanfler (2016) records the Straight Edge clean and sober punk movement that emerged among youth in the early 1980s. Wrenn (2015) discusses his religious conviction that brought him to a clean and sober life. We can see in the documentary *Heroin: Facing the Dragon* (Higson, 2010) how people who embark on a treatment at the Thamkrabok Monastery in Thailand are guided on a clean and sober path.

As a naturopath as well as a clinical hypnotherapist, I also see the profound physical damage that addicts experience due to the primary and secondary effects of their addiction, many of which are life threatening. Karch (n. d.) listed the profuse medical complications that arise from substance use and abuse of many kinds. I always tell clients we are working on "you living the best life you can have now, and since you have experienced addiction, that means becoming clean and sober for the rest of your life".

While it is fashionable for many therapy schools, government agencies and organisations to adopt a harm minimisation model of reducing the substance of abuse, reduction is still addiction, and ultimately runs the risk of leading back to a severe addiction. It is not a model of recovery but a model of abuse tolerance. In my mind, colluding with a client to create the belief that using small amounts of the substance they abuse is a case of the therapist, and particularly hypnotherapist, losing sight of their goal of being the client's guide. The client with addiction comes to the clinician for help to overcome it, not to be a half or quarter of an addict.

The clean and sober model also requires the therapist to be clean and sober. It is a great responsibility when a client comes to you for help with an addiction that may threaten their life and sanity. As a hypnotherapist you need to be congruent with the suggestions you give to clients. If you are obese and telling people to lose weight, or you do not exercise but are telling clients to exercise, you are incongruent. As an addiction therapist telling people to stop taking their substance of abuse when you are not clean and sober yourself is equally incongruent and inauthentic and your client will pick that up, both consciously and unconsciously, which can jeopardise treatment.

One of the reasons I get such high results with clients wishing to get control over their addiction is because I am 100% authentic. I teach, not preach. I do not smoke, drink alcohol or take drugs. When I sit in a room, as a hypnotist working with an addict, each suggestion I give around stopping the addiction and being clean and sober is congruent with the way I live my life. The client's conscious and unconscious awareness is reading that congruency, so the suggestion is more powerful. I am not only the guide leading the way but the person that the client understands knows the way and can model.

How is hypnotherapy influential?
Heap & Kirsch (2016) wrote about the five basic theories of how hypnosis and hypnotherapy work: the biological, social compliance, psychonanalytical, communications and integrative theories.

While they leaned towards the social compliance theory, I do not. The first three are the most explored, yet considering that any communication between human beings has the potential to be hypnotic, it is wise to treat all therapeutic communications as hypnotic. I work with the assumption that I am operating from the point of the integrative approach, under the belief that all of the first four theories are operating. It therefore follows that I conduct hypnosis from an expansionist perspective, not a reductionist one; in other words, every communication with the client is hypnotic, in or out of consciously recognised trance states.

The American psychiatrist Milton Erickson, probably the most intuitive therapeutic hypnotist of the past century, described hypnosis as the process of inducing a trance-like state (Ernest, 1980). The trance-like state is defined as an altered state of awareness other than consciousness that renders the hypnotised person more susceptible to suggestion. As we work as hypnotherapists we know this to be clearly true. Erickson also said that he believes all therapeutic hypnotists should have training as psychotherapists because hypnosis is simply the delivery vehicle by which therapy is delivered to change thought, behaviours, emotion and experience. If you truly want to work well with clients recovering from addiction, my advice is to train as a psychotherapist as well.

One of the other things that Erickson said in the case of *The February Man* (Erickson, 2009) was that he often entered into a trance with the patients he worked with. Indeed, we need as hypnotists to match, mirror and pace some of the client's physical actions such as breathing and body language, as well as linguistic style and cultural references, to gain rapport with the client's physical body and psyche to induce hypnosis. However, we must be careful never to enter into the addiction trance in which the addict is living. The Sherpa does not follow the mountain climber off the edge of the abyss but instead guides them away to a safe path.

I will expand, however, on Erickson's official perspective in that I believe all communication is hypnotic, with some states rendering the client more suggestible and others less suggestible. We are paid as hypnotherapists for inducing the official trance state but much of the work we need to do will also be out of that state. If you watch footage of Erickson working, you can see that he is conducting suggestions and eliciting change via all communication (Bruno, 2016).

Many authors have reported hypnotherapy has proved effective in substance cessation in individual and group therapy. What is offered is qualitative reporting. Qualitative reporting is valid as evidence of efficacy in medicine because quantitative reporting could not take into account the large number of variables operating in the exchange of hypnotic communications. These variables would include level of training and experience of the therapist, therapist's personality, type of induction used, linguistic style, competence in hypnotic language, the client's physical, psychological and emotional complex state, the setting in which the treatment occurred, clarification of goals and the client's ability to follow suggestion. So while teaching you the 6-Step Stop Drugs and Alcohol Clinical Hypnotherapy Model in these pages, I suggest that a hypnotic experience is never replicable and changes from client to client and session to session, so the hypnotherapist must reassess their approach in every session.

Initial contact

Hypnosis begins with your first contact with the addict. I speak to all addicts on the telephone before they come into my clinic. It is an opportunity for me to test and measure whether they are right and ready for the treatment I offer. Some people are not and I have no interest in working with those people, nor wasting their time and money.

The first kind of initial contact I encounter from addicts are people who are ready to recover from their addiction, are clear in their mind that they want help, and are prepared to do what is necessary to become free of their addiction. They telephone the clinic, book an appointment, turn up on time and therapy commences.

The second kind of contact I will encounter in private practice is the addict who is undecided. Perhaps they have seen my advert or were given a referral and want further details, or they are nervous about hypnosis and want to ask some questions. These potential clients need reassurance and what we call social proof. Since I have worked with addicts, I tell them I have worked with addicts. Since I have testimonials, I make these available to the addict, reassuring them I can help. My job is not to be pious or righteous but to facilitate their sobriety and bring them across the line to book the appointment to get help. I have already started hypnosis.

The third kind of contact is the sceptic who says they don't believe in hypnosis. Of course you wonder why they phoned. They commence by telling you about all the reasons they cannot come into treatment. It begins with the cost, although they tell you they spend four times as much per month on their addiction. Then follows their reasons why they cannot attend an appointment, regardless of whatever time and date is offered to them. We then have the various stories about unscrupulous therapists from persons unknown and unverifiable that lead to the discrediting of therapists in general. This is the completely unmotivated addict who has no intention of stopping their addiction but just thought they would telephone for someone to complain to or because they can then say to themselves or their relatives that they tried to stop. To this addict you owe nothing and if you take them on, they will sabotage the therapy. They may have to lose everything in their life before they are sufficiently motivated to stop the addiction and some may never get to that place.

The fourth contact is the relative. They come in two kinds. The first is the well-meaning relative who wishes the addict would cease their behaviour. They tell you they want their relative to stop the addiction. They are simply making enquiries for some-one else or the addict is too busy to make contact themselves. They may even want to make an appointment for the addict, dis-cuss costs and many other questions. I inform this person I am unable to discuss the case with them due to my legal liability to only discuss the case with the client, unless I have their written permission to do so or unless the addict is legally *non compos mentis* and the relative is their legal guardian. I further ask the relative to get the addict to telephone me so I can help them and say I would be happy to speak to them because only then can I find out if the addict is suitable for treatment.

The second kind of relative is angry, often has behavioural problems themselves and wishes to vent their anger on someone. I acknowledge their distress and give them the same instruction as the first kind of relative. I do not offer to see them because, if later I see the addict, I may already have had my assessment of the addict contaminated.

When I used to see patients in London paid for by the National Health Service (NHS), which is the UK's publicly funded health system, I would often see people who were less motivated to stop their addiction. This was not always the case though. There comes a point in many addicts' lives when they know they are in trouble and will reach out for any help they can get. If you work in social medicine you must also screen your potential clients because if you take on a case who is clearly not committed to stopping their addiction, you may damage the potential for them stopping the addiction later.

The question I want answered at the initial point of contact with a potential client is very clear: *"How committed are you to stopping your addiction on a percentage scale?"* For me to accept that client, they must respond with 100%. They may say 40% or 80%, at which time I tell them I only take people who are 100% committed to stopping. My response is, *"So I can wait on the phone until you get to 100%, or you can telephone me back when you are 100% committed.*" If the potential client cannot get to 100%, I do not take them. Hypnotic screening has already begun.

The contract

At the beginning of any therapy I get clients to read through and sign a written contract of agreement for therapy and the client gets a copy to take away with them (a copy of my standard contract is available at www.doctorok.com/addictionbookresources). I am aware some therapists do not think it is necessary but I believe it is part of the therapy, particularly with addicts seeking to recover. The contract covers the financial terms and conditions of therapy including the policies around payment, cancellations and fees. I started working in a health club 47 years ago and am still in business providing services to thousands of people because I am an astute business woman. I have premises, staff, an accountant, a book-keeper, insurance, professional development and other expenses to pay each year. Everyone gets paid on time so I expect clients to pay on time. A recent survey by the Psychotherapy and Counselling Federation of Australia (Lewis, 2016) found that the majority of therapists earn less than $50,000 per year which is less than the national average wage. There is an old naturopathic saying: "The well-being of the therapist adds to the well-being of the patient."

What the contract also defines is the expectations for the addict so they know what is expected of them. I am holding them accountable in writing for their actions in therapy. Addicts live a life of chaos and often mistake the circumstances of many contracts and then frequently do not want to comply with spoken contracts. When they get a copy of a written contract they have signed, they are on a surer footing around knowing about their appointments and the terms and conditions of service. Not only does it show them I expect them to be accountable *in* therapy, but also that I will be holding them accountable *during* their whole therapeutic term. Remember, miscommunication breaks rapport and clear communication builds rapport and trust.

I also require clients who come for addiction to read and sign a second contract specifically addressing their need to adhere to therapy during addiction recovery. This sets out their responsibilities as a client in recovery and holds them accountable.

Before the addict comes to see me, they are also sent a patient guide which sets out the terms and conditions under which therapy is provided and also gives them advice on how to do well in therapy. Therapy does not start in the consulting room as I am prepping people for therapy before they attend. I do not work on a system where I do not know who is coming to my office for therapy. I have screened everyone, as much as possible, before they get an appointment to determine if I will be able to help them. So conversely there are many people I turn away from therapy because I do not believe I will be able to help them because they are not suitable or sufficiently committed yet.

If you work in social medicine you may have clients coming into your office you know absolutely nothing about who have not been pre-screened for addiction recovery. Under these circumstances I also suggest you start by screening the client to see if they are suitable for addiction recovery with hypnotherapy. Your job is not to push boulders bigger than yourself up hills. How committed is the client to now recovering from their addiction?

History taking and data mining

Taking a client's history and details serves many purposes and legally, and for insurance purposes, we need to take precise notes and details. Most therapists take insufficient notes at the beginning of therapy so they are working with clients while unaware of very important information that could change the course of therapy.

When I take the history of an addict, it is extensive and in-depth so I am fully equipped to decide how to work with that client. This takes around 30 minutes. At the same time I am observing the client to see their reactions. I am testing them with humour to see how many smiles per minute they can manage, which tells me how much depression may be present, how *compos mentis* they are or whether they are presently in a disassociated substance-induced state. I am also testing them to see how susceptible to somnambulism and suggestibility they are, what resistance arises, and am looking for their major communication modalities. Much of this is done out of the client's conscious awareness.

As a naturopath I am also taking a full medical history to determine what other treatments we may need to apply in addition to hypnotherapy. Much of the information I am able to mine from the client I may be able to leverage later when looking for drivers to help the client move towards recovery. A copy of my intake form is available at www.doctorok.com/addictionbookresources.

If you are not medically trained you still need to field for medical problems in your intake process. One of the interesting events that can happen during second and third sessions is that people disclose they are taking medications they have not mentioned before.

Choosing a clinical setting

Many therapists operate from their home. When working with addiction cessation, however, I advise that therapists choose to see clients in a clinical setting. This frames therapy in a more professional setting. It gives indications that the clinical setting is where the client is expected to behave as a client, which increases compliance.

People with addiction problems may have secondary mental health problems such as acting out, becoming aggressive or violent, and stealing, so for safety reasons you would not want that in your home. The clinical setting gives you more authority so your hypnotic suggestions, when delivered correctly, can be more powerful. There are also sometimes problems from third parties who might not want the addict to stop taking the substance, who may turn up at the practice.

Clinical allies and saboteurs

Therapy happens within the context of the client's life and within their social dynamics, some of which the therapist becomes aware of and some they do not. In loading the probabilities of success for the client, it is wise for the therapist to try and understand the client's world. Satir (1988), the family therapist, talked about the roles that people fulfil within families. Sometimes they will play the underdog, subservient role or the role of the family sick person who they or other members of their family might not want to be changed.

Berne (1996) described how people adopt aggressive, submissive or egalitarian roles in their communications and ways of living. Addicts constantly adopt child-like roles, acting out and becoming aggressive when the addiction is challenged. Along with that child-like role may come many secondary gains such as receiving welfare payments, free accommodation or being ferried around by their parents or other family members or carers. There will be people around the addict who support the change to a clean and sober life and those who sabotage the client's efforts.

As the therapist you are a point of support for the recovering addict. You cannot, however, be with them 24 hours a day, even though your post-hypnotic suggestions need to be. So it is important to help the client to identify their points of support to take them towards and maintain them in a state of being clean and sober.

- Who is invested in them being clean and sober?
- Who will encourage them?
- Who will be there to support them?
- Who will be there for them in emergencies?
- Who will help protect their sobriety?

Some clients have been programmed to play the helpless victim by members of their families, family doctors, psychologists, psychiatrists, social workers, or even the social and legal system. If you give someone a label they will then begin to act out the dynamics of that label and fulfil their perceived stereotypical archetype of that label. By the time you see many clients, they are already living and acting out the archetype of being the helpless addict. They are playing the role of the addict; it is embedded in their unconscious behavioural routines and sub-routines. They are operating many thoughts and behaviours automatically, often out of their conscious awareness.

Other people, the saboteurs, are also acting out expectations that the addict behaves according to these archetypes. They are continually reinforcing that archetype in their communication with the addict, sometimes unaware they are doing that. In fact they may be invested consciously or unconsciously in the addict staying the same and they sabotage therapy by any means to fulfil their own agendas.

You need to teach your client to move towards their allies and away from their saboteurs and you need to be aware of who they are so you can guide the recovering addict.

How hypnotisable is the client?

Hypnotisability is a misnomer. The only reason to put a client through a series of hypnotisability tests such as the hand clasp, levitating arm or feet-stuck-to-the-floor test is to convince the client they are hypnotisable by using these tests as ratification of a trance-like state. These mechanisms can also be done as inductions of instant somnambulism. However, I do not use them because their association with show business and tricks can also frighten the client and make them suspicious of your professionalism.

I begin with the premise that all clients may experience hypnosis in its different forms.

(Tracie): So it's interesting when we talk about hypnosis (engagement)…everyone of course may have their own idea what hypnosis is (allowing the client to be right)…**we might like to think of hypnosis as a form of focused concentration** (indirect suggestion for focusing during hypnosis)…that may seem very confusing (trance deepener, transderivational search)…very confusing indeed (fractionation)…it's ok to be confused (ratification of the client's need to go inside to escape confusion)…isn't it (interrogative deepener)… you can enjoy hypnosis in any way that is right for you (giving the client permission to be right)…**just close your eyes and rest for a while** (direct suggestion)…you can of course focus on that rest like I'm saying (indirect suggestion to get the client to go inside)… relaxing as your body's letting itself meld into the contours of that big comfortable chair (giving up conscious control)…as you focus on relaxing every part of your body for a while (compounding and directing focus to give up consciousness)…**always hearing my voice and your body is going to sleep** (post-hypnotic suggestion for repeating suggestion)…that's good…very good…very good indeed…it seems you're good at this (ratifying the trance state)… just letting go…with every breath you relax more in hypnosis (deepening, compounding suggestion for relaxation)…**and when you are really relaxed you can open your eyes and look at me** (inducting somnambulism).

We are now working with the client in a state of somnambulism. Since I did not ask them to wake up, they will remain in a trance while I continue to explore their history.

Is the client suggestible?
Every one of us is highly suggestible. Every day we buy things from the shops that have been advertised, comply with family members' voiced desires, vote for the politician who made the best pitch to us, and pay our taxes because we were told it is the right thing to do.

The question is not how suggestible the person is in the trance state because we are always in a trance of some kind, but what is the right suggestion to make to the person at this time. I did not ask the person to go into a trance, nor did I ask them to be hypnotised; I simply asked them to concentrate their attention on relaxing. When they are relaxed I am getting them to validate the altered state of awareness by asking them to open their eyes when they are really relaxed.

(Tracie): Feeling good (direct suggestion for associating a trance with a good experience)…oh yes I can see you're very relaxed (suggestion for continuing somnambulism)…isn't that nice (interrogative suggestion for deepening)…it's pleasant to listen to suggestions (indirect suggestion for suggestibility)…**what I say can really help you** (associating suggestion compliance with goal outcomes)…you will listen to my suggestions (direct suggestion)…and feel good knowing they are helping you (direct suggestion to feel good about accepting suggestions)…just close your eyes again (suggestion for further disassociation)…**rest now rest deeper as your body relaxes more and more** (deepening suggestion)…see that's a really good suggestion you are hearing that makes you feel good (trimodality suggestion for compliance)…so suggestions are really positive experiences to follow (ratifying the acceptability of suggestions)…confused again… so confused (transderivational search)…**then just follow my suggestions** (direct suggestion for compliance)…with your eyes closed and your eyes open looking at me (contra suggestions for confusion, deepening somnambulism).

The 'yes set', 'no set', 'lock the gate' and the 'reverse set'
Many years ago I took a canal boat out on the English canal system, which goes for miles and miles. The canal system also meanders at different levels above sea level. To get the boat from one level to a higher level, you have to take it through a series of

locks. When you take the boat into the lock you have to close the gate behind you to raise the water level before you exit the lock to progress up the different levels to pass through the canal on higher ground.

As a hypnotist when you use a 'yes set' it is not enough to leave the suggestion there because, like the lock, you must also 'lock the gate' with a 'no set', after the 'yes set', before you make the next suggestion. This helps the client change the structures of their thoughts, behaviours and neural pathways, and strengthens suggestion.

Erickson on film, working with Ruth, demonstrated the 'yes set' and 'no set' (Tassotti, 2015). This classic example shows how he gave Ruth direct suggestions to nod her head for 'yes' and shake her head for 'no'.

He also demonstrated the 'reverse' set with Ruth by going on to get her to shake her head for yes and nod her head for no. What this does is demonstrate suggestion for breaking old established patterns. As a hypnotist working with addicts, you need to constantly disrupt your client's old established cognitions and behaviours in order to install new ones. When clients realise they are behaving in different ways to how they normally behave, they are ratifying the trance and the power of suggestion.

Below is an example of a 'yes set' and 'no set':

(Tracie): Maybe for a moment you can just close your eyes again since you liked relaxing so much (indirect suggestion for eye closure, ratification of trance) …that's good…really good… and when you are really relaxed…**nod your head up and down** (direct suggestion for acknowledging the relaxed trance state)… Nod your head as you remember that deep trance state…(wait for the head nod)…remember that relaxed feeling of being in trance…**that's right relaxed isn't it** (suggestion for memory recall, wait for the client to nod their head – 'yes set')…you'll enjoy feeling that relaxed again in the future won't you (post-hypnotic suggestion, wait for the client to nod their head again – 'yes set')...**relaxing more and more and more**...you just don't care about the troubles of the world at the moment do you... and you shake your head (wait for the client to shake their head again – 'no set')...in fact just at this moment you can't even remember all those troubles can you (suggestion for a negative hallucination, wait for the client to shake their head again – 'no set')...**and bring that good feeling all the way back to the room with you as you open your eyes and smile at me** (continuing the somnambulism).

While I may appear to be working intuitively I am always play-ing a game of chess with clients, manoeuvring them towards the behavioural advancement we wish to see. I have preconditioned the client to use head nods and shakes since the moment they entered the room by using nods and shakes myself each time I said yes or no. Throughout therapy I am continually using yes sets, no sets and locking the gate, and every statement and sug-gestion is thought through before it is delivered.

Are you checking your work as you go?

I generally work very fast somnambulistically with clients to put them into a continual state of confusion and cause cogni-tive overload, which renders them highly suggestible. I may offer opposing statements, mime one suggestion while presenting another or challenge their statements. When people are con-fused they must go into transderivational search to make sense of the communication, which sends them deeper into the trance state and makes them more suggestible. I am working psycho-therapeutically with hypnotic techniques.

Traditional direct suggestion hypnotists often only give sug-gestions and while that can be very useful, there is no way of knowing what change has taken place in the client's mind. It is

113

important in therapy to map the client's progress, session by session, hour by hour and minute by minute.

A standard phrase I ask hundreds of times in a session is *"Does that make sense?"* I test whether the client has accepted the suggestion, idea and cognitive change we are aiming for. If they have, we can move on to the next change, but if they have not, I need to repackage the suggestion so it is more palatable for them, and check the outcome again.

This way of checking your work is particularly important in dealing with substance abuse as the client needs to change so much of their global view of the world and themselves. Another phrase I may use when working somnambulistically is *"In what ways does this way of thinking help you?"* It carries with it the presupposition that the mindset change has happened already, does actually help them and that it helps them in many ways.

Confabulation

We continually use a process called reality testing, checking our orientation in the world. This takes place in all our senses as we gauge by heat how far we are from the fire, whether a smell is flowery or pungent, a taste sweet or sour, light is dim or bright, or sound is loud or soft. It is an information-gathering process that helps us negotiate the world and keep ourselves safe. We are also trying to work out whether someone's statement is true or false and whether we have a true assessment of what is happening in the world.

Human beings, and indeed other animals too, live in their own constructed reality. It is a false construction that comes about through our need to stop ourselves being emotionally hurt, so it is a defence mechanism. We seek to fulfil our wants, needs and desires but when the goal is not achievable, we create and maintain comfort by constructing false realities.

Everyone lies to themselves and others several times a day for many reasons. We do not like confrontation and we will do anything to maintain what we believe is a safe environment, even if a better option might be available. In the documentary *(Dis)Honesty: The Truth About Lies* (Weiss-Lurie, Schiller, & Melamede, 2015), we see university students consistently lying to achieve economic gain, and how we not only lie to cover embarrassment, but also so we do not have to face our realities. The addict has very poor reality testing. They either never had good assessment skills or, when they became addicted, they lost the ability to assess environmental dangers and benefits.

Addicts will confabulate, knowing that they are lying, misconstrue the truth, tell you what they think you want to hear, leave out information, withdraw into the addiction trance, create positive and negative hallucinations in order to protect and maintain the trance of addiction, or can become defensive and aggressive when challenged and can run away from therapy if their addiction is threatened. None of this is intentional but a feature of addictive behaviour where the addict is unable to deal with reality.

Growing the immature personality

All addicts have immature personalities without exception. Perls (1992) considered therapy as being the maturing of the personality and I agree with him. The immature personality is operating in a child-like mode. The child is dependent, requiring other people and objects to satisfy their need for security and fulfilment. In fact, we are programmed as children to believe that we must rely on adults and consumerism to survive. Advertising conditions us so that we must consume objects in order to be satisfied as a whole person. This includes houses, cars, boats, aeroplanes, holidays, clothes, jewellery, alcohol and drugs.

The mature personality, which for most people does not develop until their early forties, is self-sufficient and self-contained. It does not require so many of the things we seek when we are young. Neither is it as vulnerable to the vagaries of the world and life. When disaster strikes, the mature personality goes through the initial trauma, reassesses, repairs and reinvents itself. It is independent, developmental, adaptive, self-sufficient and grown-up.

The addict relies on the substance of addiction for security and fulfilment. It is not just an adventure but a dependency. The addict has come to rely on the substance to recreate homeostasis, and normalcy. However, this is a delusion because the very act of being addicted means that homeostasis and normalcy no longer exist. In working with addicts we must help them grow their personalities to become more mature and independent of the substance on which they came to rely. Only when the addict becomes clean and sober and mature can they independently fulfil their needs for security and fulfilment, and become free from addiction.

Chapter 4 References

Alcoholics Anonymous World Services, Inc. (2001). *Alcoholics anonymous* (4th ed.). New York, NY: Author.

American Psychiatric Association. (2013). *Diagnostic and statistical manual of mental disorders* (5th ed.). Arlington, VA: Author.

Berne, E. (1996). *Games people play: The basic handbook of transactional analysis.* New York, NY: Ballantine Books.

Bowling, B., & Phillips, C. (2007). Disproportionate and discriminatory: Reviewing the evidence on police stop and search. *The Modern Law Review Limited, 70*(6), 936–961.

Bruno S. (2016, May 2). *Milton Erickson – Clinical session – November 1958 – Subtitled!* [Video file]. Retrieved from https://www.youtube.com/watch?v=NeXhTfN8okE

Erickson, M. (2009). *The February man: Evolving consciousness and identity in hypnotherapy.* Abingdon, United Kingdom: Routledge.

Ernest, R. (Ed.). (1980). *The nature of hypnosis and suggestion: The collected papers of Milton H. Erickson on hypnosis, Vol. 1.* New York, NY: Irvington.

Heanfler, R. (2016). *Straight edge: Hardcore punk, clean living youth, and social change.* New Brunswick, NJ: Rutgers University Press.

Heap, M., & Kirsch, I. (2016). *Hypnosis.* Farnham, United Kingdom: Ashgate.

Higson, R. (Director & Producer). (2010). *Heroin: Facing the dragon* [Television documentary]. San Francisco, CA: Current TV.

Karch, S. B. (n.d.). *Addiction and the medical complications of drug abuse* [Kindle version]. Retrieved from Amazon.com

Lewis, I. (2016). Australian counselling and psychotherapy workforce study 2015 update report. *PACFA eNewsletter*. Retrieved from http://www.pacfa.org.au/wp-content/uploads/2016/08/eNews-July-2016.pdf

Perls, F. S. (1992). *Gestalt therapy verbatim*. Gouldsboro, ME: The Gestalt Journal Press.

Satir, V. (1988). *The new peoplemaking* (2nd ed.). Palo Alto, CA: Science and Behavior Books.

Tassotti, F. [Fiorenzo Tassotti]. (2015, July 8). *Milton H Erickson the reverse set in hypnotic induction* [Video file]. Retrieved from https://www.youtube.com/watch?v=4RILCNNEQU4

Vaughan, G., & Hogg, M. A. (2014). *Social psychology* (7th ed.). Harlow, England: Pearson.

Weiss-Lurie, C., Schiller, M. (Executive producers), & Melamede, Y. (Director). (2015). *(Dis)honesty: The truth about lies* [Film]. New York, NY: Salty Features.

World Health Organization. (2011). *International statistical classification of disease and related health problems* (4th ed.). Geneva, Switzerland: Author.

Wrenn, M. (2015). *God's addiction recovery plan: The biblical path to freedom*. Bloomington, IN: WestBow.

5 *Stay Out of Denial*

There are two kinds of people you will work with who need recovery from their addiction: those with voluntary commitment to recovery and those with persuaded commitment to recovery. Both can do well in recovery and each must be approached differently. Voluntary recovering addicts have already stated their desire to stop using their substance of abuse. It is clear in their statements, language, speech patterns and body language that they are ready to stop their addiction with your help. This has become obvious to you during the pre-screening. They may even have been in other recovery programs that have failed for them but when they come to you they already have the mindset that they now wish to become clean and sober.

The second kind of client you will work with is the persuaded recovering addict. This client may have come to see you for other reasons, and while you are taking their history or during therapy, you discover they have a substance abuse problem. They may be aware of the problem but have not mentioned it, are too embarrassed to disclose, or simply do not think it is a problem for them and has no bearing on what else is happening in their lives.

As a clinician you can see that substance abuse may be a central core of or contributor to the problems the client is presenting with, so it would be judicious to stop the substance while they are trying to sort out their other problems. I am very direct with clients around this situation. As therapists we are duty bound to tell our clients what we observe, just as if we were a quantity surveyor or business analyst. Hetero-hypnosis, hypnotherapy, and change in the client is based on a trustful relationship and that needs to be congruent with all the hypnotist's communications. A client might not initially like something you may say to them but if you frame and reframe it in a palatable way and validate the veracity of the statement, they will be more likely to respect you and trust you.

> Bobby: I've come to see you because I'm in trouble with the law again. The boss I work for suggested I get some help. All right, he told me if I didn't get some help to stay out of trouble with the cops, he'd sack me because it was bad for the reputation of his business. He says if I mess up when repairing a vehicle and am affected by drugs, he could be sued. He went to court before to say I behaved myself at work and I didn't take drugs at work but he said I've run out of chances.

All treatment for addiction must start with keeping the client safe physically, mentally, emotionally, and following the Hippocratic Oath's principle of 'do no harm'. The client comes into therapy dysfunctional, distressed and troubled by their own experiences. Lurking in the addict's mind is a sense of conflict, doubt, trauma, anger, sadness, humiliation and past memories that we do not know about and maybe even they do not consciously remember. An abreaction can release those memories and traumas at any time, during or after the session.

Addicts are traumatised people. The body is out of synchronicity with nature, homeostasis has been disturbed, and the addict is unable to rebalance their body and life patterns. Medically, psychologically, and maybe even socially, they are in trauma. Many addicts have also experienced other traumas early in life such as child sexual abuse, bullying, violence or abandonment by their parents. Some addicts know they are in trauma, but some do not, such as cocaine and amphetamine users, who often have a sense of invincibility or even grandiosity.

Machovec (2012) writes about the damage done to clients during hypnosis by negligent therapists and how uncontrolled release of memories can cause hypnotically induced psychotic decompression. Complications can also happen accidentally when the hypnotherapist has taken all reasonable precautions. I wrote in my book, *Investigating Stage Hypnosis,* about the damage experienced by participants involved in stage hypnosis who were not pre-screened for potential psychopathy, failed to have suggestions cancelled or who were unable to cope with the hypnotic experience (O'Keefe, 1998). In my opinion, a young mother, Sharron Tabarn, died hours after a stage hypnosis show as a result of heart failure due to an apparent uncancelled suggestion for electric shock.

At the beginning of therapy I always install a safety anchor (cue/response mechanism) to elicit the client's ability to feel safe when I trigger that anchor (cue). You may associate the trigger in any of the three major sensory modalities of auditory, visual or kinaesthetic. A visual external cue is probably not good if the client has their eyes closed. Hearing is the last sense to go before death so it is probably the most immediate cue to trigger. I tend to put a kinaesthetic anchor on the back of the left hand with everyone so I can remember where it is and, as an older woman, I am seen as less threatening in touching the client; however, male hypnotherapists may need to be a little more cautious in installing physical anchors.

Safety anchor intentions

1. It is important when working with clients to install in them, right at the beginning of therapy, the sense that you as a therapist are safe to work with.

2. Clients can abreact at any time during therapy and at that time you need to be able to trigger the safety anchor to

bring them back to a place and time of safety.

3. Clients can regress or progress to trauma at any time during trance work, so you need to be able to trigger the safety anchor to bring them back to a place and time of safety.

4. Clients can enter into psychotic decompression at any time during or after trance work, so you need to be able to trigger the safety anchor to bring them back to a place and time of safety.

5. Safety anchors can be triggered during trance work.

6. Safety anchors are best installed in Ve, Ae or Ke modality systems. Male therapists working with female clients may be more comfortable not using Ke anchors to avoid confusion around physical contact.

Installing a safety anchor

(Tracie): Close your eyes and go inside…Bobby just for a while as you sit still there in that chair (catalepsy)…you can take the time to rest (time disorientation, taking the client out of fight or flight)…**closing your eyes as my voice goes with you** (contingent suggestion for Ai presence of therapist's voice and hypnotic repetition of suggestion loop)…that's right so good (orientation to good Ki+)…in a moment I am going to ask you to take three deep breaths (preparation for suggestion)…**take a huge breath now and fill your lungs – 1** (kinaesthetic control, intrahypnotic suggestion)…and hold it (gathering resistance)…with your mouth open just let it go so easy (command compliance for relaxation and experiencing safety)…**and a second deep breath – 2** (creating a yes set through repetition)…bring all the rest of the tension into your body (draining remaining resistance)… let it all out through your mouth (compounding dependence on the hypnotist for safety)…**gently and slowly a third deep breath** (preparing for completing the yes set for relaxation)…and slowly letting it all go (trance deepener)…**as your body deeply lets go... Good…Very Good** (rewarding the yes set behaviour)…continuing to focus on your gentle breathing as I speak (linking hypnotist's voice to safety)…in…and out…you can be aware of being here in Sydney (truism)…**safe in my office** (suggestion for situational safety)…in Surry Hills…my funny little office…**so safe in my office** (fractionation)…in a moment I'm going to reach across and touch you on the back of the left hand…(preparation for installing the safety anchor on the out breath) **that's right so safe in my office** (compounding the anchor Ki+, Ke+ and situational)…whenever, wherever, if ever I touch the back of your left hand (ratifying the anchor)…again…**instantly you can feel safe** (touch back of left hand again on the out breath).

Weitzenhoffer (2000) criticised Erickson's work with the subject Ruth, shown on film, which I referred to in chapter four when Erickson was demonstrating the 'reverse set'. The premise of the criticism was that the subject Ruth was not really in trance or somnambulistic. Many hypnotists believe that somnambulism must be preceded by partly awakening the subject after a deep, unconscious trance state and must be followed by amnesia. In my experience, this is not necessary.

The signs of hypnotically induced somnambulism are that the subject is engaged with the hypnotist, compliant to suggestion, has their eyes open, is not unduly distracted by external stimuli and can demonstrate catatalepsy on demand. While the waking trance state can occur through suggestion after a soporific trance state, it is also induced via a waking hypnotic suggestion, creating instant somnambulism.

Inexperienced hypnotists are often afraid of using instant somnambulism, particularly if a suggestion fails, because they have been trained to induce sleeping trance states. As soon as the client enters the office I am working with them somnambulistically and I advise clinical hypnotherapists to do the same. For all hypnotists, some suggestions fail and as the hypnotherapist observes the failure, they must reconstitute the suggestion or try another suggestion to implement the cognitive, behaviour or emotional change.

> Tracie: *You know Bobby sometimes the universe is giving you a message. Your own birth father ran away when you were young. Your boss sounds a pretty stand-up guy. After all he stood by you once before when you were in trouble and you still have a job at the moment. You told me he had been like a father to you when you were doing your mechanical engineering apprenticeship. Yep, you know Bobby, I think I like your boss. He has been good for you in many ways so I wonder if he still has your well-being in mind now in trying to get you to sort out your life?*

Dealing with resistance

Fielding resistance intentions

1. Resistance to change of behaviour may arise at any time during therapy or between therapy sessions.
2. All resistance to change in therapy is a defence mechanism resulting from unconscious conflict that may or may not transpire in conscious behaviour.
3. Challenging resistance directly runs the risk of increasing the efforts of the conscious defence mechanisms in defending the addiction.
4. Sometimes the intentions of the defensive part may need to be elicited (hypnoanalytically) to be dealt with and sometimes not (unconscious resolution).
5. Sometimes parts negotiation may be sufficient to overcome resistance to behavioural change.
6. Your job as a therapist is to help clients deal with resistance to behavioural change as it arises.

Bobby: You know, I don't think I'm an addict. I hold down a job. Only take cocaine on weekends. My mates do the same thing. We just do it to party. All the guys in my area do it. It's like normal. Everybody does it, don't they? I want to still be able to take some cocaine.

Tracie: Mmm…just let me check your notes. You've been taking cocaine on weekends for four years. You told me you've been busted using cocaine while driving. It's the third time. You'll probably lose your driving licence and might face prison. You're also on bail for your seventh charge of assault and battery for fighting in night clubs. You're actually on a suspended sentence at the moment that you may have to serve when you go to court. Your girlfriend has split up with you because she complains you don't pay her enough attention; your mother and stepfather won't talk to you or receive you at their house; you're not allowed to see your younger brother; and you may be in danger of losing your job…so how's that going for you? Just maybe your behaviour has descended into a drug-fuelled paranoid violence… hey Bobby, what do you think?

Bobby: I suppose you have a point.

Tracie: All I'm doing is repeating back to you what you told me…tell me, if you were sitting in my seat, what would you think? …Would you think the guy in front of me had his head in the sand, wanting not to see the world, needed a big wake up call, was deluding himself, and just maybe could lead a better life, stop getting in trouble with the law, cease beating people up, stay out of jail and *keep a girlfriend if perhaps he was not sticking white powder up his nose, pretending he was not an addict and that his mates were normal? Are you ready to carry on now? 100 percent committed to being clean and sober for life? (Interrogative overload can force people out of their delusions).*

Selling the case to the client intentions

1. Clients need help in solidifying their ideas and intentions for the outcomes of therapy.
2. They need help to overcome their resistance to their outcomes. What people say they want is not always cognitively congruent with their expected outcomes.
3. Working with people somnambulistically, you can help them achieve clarity, solidify their goals and overcome resistance that is out of conscious, hypercritical awareness.

Selling the case to the client – somnambulistically
(Tracie): Bobby you have had a problem (truism, time shift and acknowledging their difficulties)…that problem has caused you pain and brought you here (truism and association of old behaviour to undesired outcome)…**you can appreciate your need to clean up your act…can't you NOW** (interrogative suggestion, forcing a cognitive shift (I nod my head, then he nods his head – yes set for clean and sober)…of course getting here was a big journey (empathically acknowledging struggle and pain)…and you made it (ego strengthening)…**NOW is the time**…(time framing to the present – suggestion for instant change)…**to change who and what you are** (demand for complete change)…. **becoming clean and sober** (direct suggestion)…living your goal (reaffirming the goal)…free to live your brilliant life (future pacing – positive emotional driver)…**clean and sober** (affirming clean and sober, repetition, normalising sobriety).

All of us as therapists have been trained by different teachers in different styles of hypnotherapy. Many of us are multi-disciplinary, so we cross-fertilise what we do as therapists to combine techniques to facilitate different clients' needs. Many decades ago at college when I was 15, we used co-counselling, as taught to us by a local psychiatrist, in a student support group I set up. It was based on work by Jackins (1962/2001) and we sat in a circle, with each student taking turns being the counsellor and adviser to others in the group. While it was very supportive, it lacked direction for those in trouble. It was a process based on a sympathetic, not solution-focused approach, and frequently lacked dynamic direction.

When we look at Maltz's (2015) cybernetics work involving visualisations and self-imagining, we can see that behavioural change that is specifically goal-directed produces greater change faster. Since its theory was based mainly around the self-help movement, the mechanics demanded greater economy of theory and increased attachment to moving change forward. His approach was to steer the mind to a productive, useful goal to reach inner peace. As hypnotherapists we need to be pre-possessed with helping to move change forward expediently for our clients.

The shopping list

It is important at the outset of all therapy to help clients clearly identify their goals. Only when those goals are clearly identified and stated does the client and the therapist know where therapy must go and what outcomes are needed. Simply sitting and talking about the addiction does not serve the client; it serves to strengthen the concept that the client is a helpless addict. The client needs empathy and help to get to those goals, not sympathy.

The shopping list intentions

1. The addiction client generally comes to therapy for addiction cessation with vague goals and the therapist can help

them clarify those goals.

2. Explain to the client the need for them to clearly know what their goals are, so they can know when they have reached them.
3. Help the client bring those goals down to a list of singular words, or only a few words per item.
4. Get the client to voice the goals before they write them.
5. Help the client to reduce long-winded goals and congratulate them every time they produce an item on the list.

> Tracie: So Bobby thank you for all those details you have given me about your history (acknowledgment of co-operation and suggestive compliance)…that's really really useful and I have a much better picture of your situation thank you so much (acknowledging the client's importance and competence)…
> **let's focus on your goals** (creating therapeutic alliance)…The next logical question for me to ask you is how can we help you (active listening and strengthening the therapeutic alliance)

The client will then tell me why they have come to therapy and occasionally they may have a written list. Some clients will focus only on their problems and not state their goal, and if this is observed, it is important to gently guide them back to goal-focused therapy and clarifying desired outcomes. Addicts may not state that they wish to cease their addiction, so it is important to get them to state clearly that they wish to stop the addiction.

(Tracie): OK Bobby I like to do an exercise with people right at the beginning of therapy (we have officially started therapy)…it's called the 'Shopping list' and is an exercise in clarifying what (indirect suggestion that an outcome will be gained)…**you want, need or desire from therapy** (initiating drivers)…you write down 1, 2, 3, 4, onwards all the things you want, need or desire from therapy (suggestion response training)…we talk about each item as you bring it down to a concise concept (training the client to be goal-directed)…**tell me what is the first item** (testing for direct command responsiveness – if the client writes before they speak, you know they are dissociated and go inside during communications so you must repeat your spoken commands).

I help the client work through the list of goals and, with an addict, the number one item on the top of the list is always to be clean and sober. During recovery therapy you must bring the client back to this concept again and again.

(Tracie): You know Bobby that's a great list and I want you to go through it and tell me which item is the most important goal that needs to go to the top (eliciting criteria of needs)…**thank you that's right clean and sober** (indirect suggestion for being clean and sober)…you are so right because it is the one action that helps you achieve all the other goals (truism)…it is your number one goal always… (re-enforcing the criteria of needs priority)… **wherever you are and whatever you are doing being clean and sober** (direct suggestion)…brilliant are you ready to continue… (pre-supposition therapy is already in progress, training command responsiveness).

Step 1: Stay Out of Denial

In the first two-hour session I spend with addicts, I teach them the first three steps of the 6-Step Program. I leave steps four, five and six until the second session, so clients are able to manage simple, initial steps to help them stop the substance use. They are exposed to steps one, two and three, over and over again during the first session to form those new neural pathways in the brain. Repetition and rehearsal is how we learn to crawl, walk, talk, run, recite the alphabet, read, comprehend and execute complex tasks. I am training and retraining the client's automatic responses.

An addict or substance abuser is not a consciously rational person or unconsciously rational person. Their decision-making skills are impaired, both physically and mentally, even though the client might present as a highly functional person and sometimes may be a great achiever academically, career-wise or in business.

If the addict was functional, they would be able to make the conscious decision not to use the substance of abuse. At some level the client knows the addiction is hurting them, but when they come into contact with the substance, they enter into a state of denial.

Step 1: Stay Out of Denial is the very foundation of the six-step pyramid that clients build inside their mind to become clean and sober. It is the first step of a chain reaction you are installing in the client. This step must always be operational because if the client goes into denial, the pyramid collapses and they go back to substance abuse.

Sigmund Freud (1990) talked about the id being the primitive instinct and even aggressive part of the psyche that seeks pleasure. The superego part of the psyche contains societal values and our internal values by which we live. These keep us safe in the world and give us moral codes, which would also contain our values around using intoxicating substances. The ego is the negotiator between the id and the superego. It helps us negotiate between the desires of the id and the regulation set down by the superego.

In addiction the id has taken over, aggressively seeking pleasure and avoidance of pain, even the ordinary, everyday pain of living. The ego is damaged by the addiction and not negotiating properly between the id and the superego. There are insufficient regulatory mechanisms and values operating in the superego to regulate the id's desire for the substance. So the id has become like the unsupervised child let loose in the chocolate factory who eats themselves to death.

Anna Freud (1992) revised her father Sigmund Freud's description of denial as a primitive defence mechanism. It is the mind protecting you from the perception that you may have previously been wrong or what you are doing now is wrong. The ego is fragile and we may even put ourselves in physical danger in order to protect the integrity of the ego, sometimes even when another part of us knows we are in danger. The addict is always in danger when they are unaware they are in denial.

Since the using addict is in a constant state of denial about their addiction, even though they may seem fully conscious of the addiction, they are in a permanent state of danger. Indeed, the mind is protecting their ego state of addiction rather than their body. It is a case of better the devil you know (the addiction) rather than take the risk of changing and perhaps failing when clean and sober. The job of the therapist is to help the client stay out of denial and be aware of the danger the substances they abuse possesses for them.

Robertson (2013) describes cognitive behavioural hypnotherapy as the mechanism of installing new thoughts and behaviours. They need to be triggered when encountering a stimulus, which in this case would be drugs or alcohol. The awareness of that trigger sets off the chain reaction of the six steps of recovery every time the person encounters the stimulus. So for all intents and purposes we are hypnotically installing a new Pavlovian response.

> Tracie: *It's interesting Bobby how you are fed up with the*
> *old behaviours that addiction has pushed you into.*
> *It's gone on for far too long and you are getting*
> *bored with it apart from it disturbing your life.*
> *In helping you stop the addiction I am going to*
> *put you on the 6 Step Stop Drugs and Alcohol*
> *Clinical Hypnotherapy Program. Today we are*
> *going to focus on the first three steps. The next*

time I see you we will talk about steps four, five and six. Today the first three steps will help you stop taking the substance. Step one is called 'Staying Out of Denial'. It is the most important step. Think of the six steps as being like a pyramid. At the bottom of the pyramid, holding up the pyramid, is Step 1 'Staying Out of Denial'. It is the step on which all other steps rest. When that step is operating well, it supports all the other steps. If there is ever a time you slip into the belief again that you are not an addict and pretend it's OK to take the substance, you risk your sobriety and clean and sober life. When Step 1 is not working, the whole pyramid collapses. So it is really important that Step 1 is working all of the time, the whole of your life, 24 hours per day, seven days a week, 365 days a year, for life. It's great that you're getting this Bobby. Really good. You're working well.

Step 1 - Staying Out of Denial intentions

1. People imbibe and create false beliefs that have no reality-testing verification, therefore they are delusions. Your job as a therapist is to demythologise the client's delusions.
2. Addicts build their realities on delusions.
3. A major tenet of addiction recovery is to teach the client to operate good reality testing. This disables those delusional trances and installs trances that operate astute reality testing.
4. Clients need to be aware, at all times, of the reality of the danger of taking addictive substances.
5. Denial is when the client goes back into the delusion that taking the substance will not seriously harm them and their lives.
6. Clients need to be cognitively aware consciously and uncon-

sciously, which helps them immediately recognise denial (Pavlovian response).

7. As a therapist you need to install in the client's unconscious mind the association between the proximity to addictive substances and being aware that taking those substances would put the client into denial.

8. You need to install in the unconscious mind the ability to stay out of denial automatically.

Step 1 – Staying Out of Denial trance script

(Tracie): Close your eyes and go inside...Bobby let's not pretend the substance is not messing up your life ('as if' frame)...let's not pretend it's not having a detrimental effect on your body (Fritz Perls' awareness perception)...**it's time for you to be real now** (suggestion, forcing the maturation process forward)... you know I'm never going to lie to you don't you (transderivational search, creating trust, establishing authority, suggestion for reality testing)...coming to see me and sitting in that chair for your reasons is really very serious (truism, forcing reality testing)...**you're going to hear it like I tell it as that's what you pay me for** (appealing for unconscious attention)...you're an addict (truism)...your life is in a mess (truism)...your body and health are in a mess (truism)...**time for you to stay out of denial 24/7/365 for the rest of your life** (behavioural change suggestion)...denial will lie to you (truism)...it will dress itself up as anything to trick you into taking that substance (truism)...'Oh I deserve a treat', 'It's been a hard day', 'I deserve a reward', 'Just this once' (transderivational search)...**your job is to look out for denial** (direct suggestion)...to see and hear its lies and to challenge them (direct suggestion, Vi&e and Ai&e self-monitoring, cognitive awareness)...to know when you feel like taking that substance it is denial (Ki&e, self-monitoring, cognitive awareness)...**your job is to stay out of denial** (direct suggestion)...nod your head if for you denial is never acceptable (direct suggestion, programming the super-ego, wait for the nod)…nod your head if it is really true (transderivational search, wait for the yes set)…will it always be true (transderivational search, wait for the yes set)… shake your head if there will never be an exception (transderivational search, wait for the no set)…**so if there will never be a time when it's OK for you to take that substance shake your head** (transderivational search, direct interrogative suggestion, wait for the no set, locking the gate).

Part of Step 1 is to install or re-install the values and regulator into the superego, giving the ego a chance to repair and negotiate healthily once again between the id and the superego. This works best when we install a strong, clear archetype part into the superego to regulate the substance use. I have developed the use of the imagery of the soldier on duty installed into the client's unconscious. It works very well to restore the control the superego has over the id. As children we are trained to obey commands and respect authority, even when we are displaying anti-social behaviour. Not only is that imagery demanding of immediate attention and respect, but it is also parental.

Firestone (2010) in *Psychology Today* wrote that being a good therapist requires the same skills as being a good parent. I believe this is correct for whatever the client comes to see you about. In the case of addiction, the therapist taking the nurturing and guiding role is essential to redirect the client towards living a clean and sober life. Sometimes the 'parent' needs to use indirect suggestion but sometimes very direct suggestion. Fromm & Shor (1979) discussed how, from a psycho-analytical theoretical perspective, hypnosis is a form of regression and we, the hypnotists, are taking the parent role.

> Tracie: You know Bobby at one time you understood
> what danger was. You knew not to put your fin-
> gers on the hot stove. Perhaps you were taught as

a child to look both ways before you crossed the road. When you swim in the sea you know not to go out too far because the rip tides may carry you away. So you do know what danger is and to avoid danger. There was even a time when you knew the dangers of taking drugs. That part that knew drugs were dangerous for you is still inside you and needs some help now to take care of you again. Let's help it. Let's help it now.

Installing the en garde part intentions

1. Freud talked about the superego which is the critical and moralising role in our unconscious. In the addict, the super-ego is failing to do its job of recognising and categorising the addictive substances as dangerous and not acceptable.

2. Installing the en garde part in the superego reactivates its job of classifying the addictive substances as dangerous and unacceptable.

3. The en garde part operates within Step 1, and when it spots the danger of addictive substances, automatically lets the person know they are in danger or in denial.

4. The en garde part is a mechanism of constant cognitive awareness for life.

Installing the en garde part trance script

(Tracie): Close your eyes and go inside…You know Bobby there is a group of soldiers in the French Army called the Foreign Legion who camp out in the desert...do you know about them (transderivational search)…when they camp out in the desert they form a circle around the camp and stand on guard (metaphor)…**just like your mind is going to learn to do that now** (direct suggestion for unconscious learning)…close your eyes and imagine that up inside your mind (Vi simulation)…when a stranger approaches the camp they say 'En

garde, who goes there, friend or foe?' (metaphor for protection)…
I want you to look up inside your mind now and put your own soldier there to protect you (visualisation, direct suggestion, trance deepener, installing defence mechanism)…your soldier is on duty 24/7/365 for the rest of your life protecting you…and whenever you come in contact with those substances in future (future pace)…**your soldier says en garde and sounds an alarm to pull you out of denial** (direct suggestion, awareness regulator)…automatically whenever… wherever…however you come into contact with that substance your en garde part sounds the alarm (suggestion for multi-time use, situational suggestion, circumstance regulation of cognitive awareness)… and you come out of denial (cognitive awareness)…**automatically your soldier is on duty in your unconscious mind always** (direct suggestion for cognitive monitoring)…**automatically**…**automatically** (installation of Pavlovian response).

When I originally saw Bobby he was near to his date to appear back in court. I worked with him on Steps 1, 2 and 3 of the 6-Step Program. He went away with a 10-minute auditory recording to use four times a day. He was due to come back and see me two weeks later but was sent to prison.

I saw him 19 months later when he had got out of prison after serving 18 months. He was allowed to keep his recording on his iPod which he used every day in prison. He did this because he told me that drugs were just as available in prison as they were on the street, so he was trying to keep himself safe by being clean and sober and fully aware of what was happening. Initially he wanted to stop getting in trouble and was persuaded to become clean and sober in order not to be on drugs when he went to court, but he stayed clean until I saw him again.

Prison had frightened him as there were career criminals in there who were far more violent than he had been. It had the effect on him of quelling his violent streak and making him a much quieter and cautious person. The only person who visited him in prison was his grandmother who never missed a visiting opportunity. His mother and stepfather still wanted nothing to do with him and he had seen his brother only once since coming out of prison.

In the second session we focused on Steps 4, 5 and 6 of the program. I saw him one more time before he left the country with his grandmother to go to India to live with his uncle and start his life again. When he asked me if he should go, I told him I could not decide for him but to consider that his old life had not worked out for him. Just maybe a new start in a new place with people who were clean and sober would help him stay clean and sober.

Firestone, L. (2010, October 31). Being a good therapist and being a good parent require the same skills. *Psychology Today*. Retrieved from https://www.psychologytoday.com

Freud, A. (1992). *The ego and the mechanics of defence*. London, England: Karnac Books.

Freud, S. (1990). *The ego and the id*. New York, NY: W. W. Norton.

Fromm, E., & Shor, R. E. (Eds.). (1979). *Hypnosis developments in research and new perspectives* (2nd ed.). Chicago, IL: Aldine.

Jackins, Harvey (2001). *Fundamentals of co-counseling manual* (4th ed.). Seattle, WA: Rational Island. (Original work published 1962)

Machovec, F. J. (2012). *Hypnosis complications: Prevention and risk management*. Bloomington, IN: iUniverse.

Maltz, M. (2015). *Psycho-cybernetics*. New York, NY: Perigee.

O'Keefe, T. (1998). *Investigating stage hypnosis*. Randwick, NSW, Australia: Extraordinary People Press.

Robertson, D. (2013). *The practice of cognitive-behavioural hypnotherapy*. London, England: Karnac Books.

Tassotti, F. [Fiorenzo Tassotti]. (2015, July 8). Milton H Erickson the reverse set in hypnotic induction [Video file]. Retrieved from https://www.youtube.com/watch?v=4RILCNNEQU4

Weitzenhoffer, A. M. (2000). *The practice of hypnotism* (2nd ed.). New York, NY: John Wiley & Sons.

6 *Stop Taking the Substance*

Some clinicians or students of hypnotherapy reading this book may have experienced taking drugs, have had addictions or alcohol problems. Others may have spent a lot of their career working with addicts. Still further there will be those of you who have never taken drugs or drunk alcohol who know nothing of the world or culture of addiction. Some of you may be very comfortable working with addiction and some may be afraid to work in this field.

The addiction is not about you, the therapist. It is a medical emergency for the client and, just as with any medical emergency, you need to follow processes, procedures and protocols. It is easy for the therapist to get lost in the chaotic world of the addict or to be overwhelmed when the client does not follow a prescribed path, so you must have systems and you must be able to adapt the therapy when systems need to be changed.

Much of the research and philosophy around stopping an addiction is mythical and entrenched in the terminology of the discipline. That knowledge is often more connected to the needs of the therapist or scientist maintaining their clinical philosophy, rather than facilitating the client's need to stop taking the substance. As therapists we need to constantly learn and change as we mature as clinicians.

Dick & Agrawal (2008) proclaimed that drug and alcohol addiction in many cases has a genetic link. While it is true that addiction can occur and become a pattern in families, we must ask: Why is it that addiction is often not expressed until cultural and social circumstances change?

The interesting thing is that, as of the time of writing, no geneticist can pinpoint any particular gene or combination of genes that causes addiction. The suggestion that addiction has a genetic cause, however, medicalises addictive behaviours. This gives free reign for expensive drugs to be promoted, for both preventing addiction and treating alcoholism. It also opens up enormous treatment profits to the medical profession, which keeps the patient sick for life and is a constant source of income for the medical establishment and the pharmaceutical companies. This does not specifically have to be medication for drugs or alcoholism; it can be anti-depressants or sedatives that have not actually been tested or proven to work for addiction.

Frank, Moore, & Ames (2000) suggest that the roots of the Native American epidemic of alcohol-related problems did not start until the arrival of Europeans in North America. They note that the level of alcoholism has been six times higher in Native American cultures than in the general population. Since the Native Americans had access to making alcohol previously, without an alcohol epidemic, how then could this epidemic have come about?

History records that Native Americans and in particular Mexican Native Americans had more than 40 alcoholic drinks before Europeans arrived but alcoholism on the scale of today did not exist in their cultures. Indeed, alcoholism has been the result of cultural displacement and the intense pressure of racism these people experience in the name of profit derived from sequestration of their lands as they suffer intergenerational trauma.

The World Health Organization (2014) in its Fourth Global Status Report on Alcohol shows tables where countries such as Belarus consume 17.5 litres of alcohol per capita per year for persons over 15; yet Mauritania and Pakistan consume only 0.1 litres per capita. Are the genetics of these populations so different? The truth is, there are few genetic differences between these cultures so this leads us clearly to the concept of drug addiction and alcoholism being the result of cultural influences and social programming or lack of learning. Some races or individuals can have smaller livers than others, or slower kidneys, leading to slower detoxification of alcohol and causing more intense intoxication. Intoxication and a hangover for many people, however, is an unpleasant experience and they do not wish to do that regularly or repeat the experience. Yet we have cultures such as Native Americans and Aboriginal Australians who are ignoring those physically unpleasant effects and experiencing high levels of alcoholism.

> Tracie: So just let me recap Mary. You are 51 years old, a lawyer between jobs, divorced 10 years ago, not seeing anyone, overweight, depressed, looking for work but afraid of interviews and are and have been drinking a bottle or two of red wine a night for several years. You've got a lot going on haven't you? Let's see what we can do to help you. Is doing that today OK?.

> Mary: That would be great Tracie. I'm just so afraid. There's not a day gone by for years when I haven't had a drink. The divorce was horrible. He ran off with someone else. I was devastated. He's never even said sorry. Then my mum died and my dad died three weeks later. I just got so depressed and started drinking every day. I'm fat, unemployed and hate myself. Now I can't stop drinking.

People buy into their own self-limiting beliefs about their abilities to do or not do something. We are all subject to the programming we have received as children. Deep in our unconscious minds are thousands of gestalts, memes and reams of suggestions that have been delivered to us over a lifetime pertaining to our abilities and expected inabilities. Rohsenow (1983) administered an alcohol effects questionnaire to 150 college students, which showed women expected and experienced less pleasure and tension reduction. They also experienced more cognitive and motor impairment from alcohol. Women's low self-expectations of their abilities seemed to add to the physiological reduced motor skills and cognitive processing.

It was Bandura (1997) who introduced the concept of perceived self-efficacy around cognitive behaviour change. It has been found that a strong sense of self-efficacy is directly related to better health outcomes. The addict has lost self-efficacy in their own behaviour to be clean and sober and experience good health, although they may be confident in being great achievers in other areas of their lives. The addicts who are able to quit the addiction on their own have a greater sense of self-efficacy. The substance abuser who does not have that self-efficacy has developed a self-fulfilling prophecy that they are a helpless addict and slave to the substance of abuse. It is the job of the hypnotherapist to install or restore in the client's unconscious mind that sense of self-efficacy.

Tracie: *In Step 1, Stay Out of Denial you will always remember that your en garde part will be with you 24/7/365 for the rest of your life. We did of course say you are stopping drinking today Mary. It seems you have punished Mary enough for your husband leaving you and your parents dying. Time is a ticking (pointing at my wrist where a watch would be). You're 51 years old with no time to waste. Time to get your life back on track. Today is the day you stop drinking. Not tomorrow, the day after or in three weeks' time. The time you stop drinking is NOW!*

142

Mary: When I worked for a law firm I was really
        dedicated. I bought my own apartment and
        had money saved for my retirement. I'm always
        afraid of what people will think of me. No one I
        worked with ever knew I had a problem with al-
        cohol. I never drank at functions because I knew
        once I started I'd never be able to stop so I'd leave
        early and go home and drink. Everyone I've ever
        worked for has really appreciated my work but
        my drinking got so bad a few months ago that
        I had to resign from my job and take time out.
        You're my last hope.

Tracie: Hope is for the nuns. Today you stop drinking.

People are led to believe quitting drugs and alcohol is going to be catastrophically hard, but let us look at the use of heroin and opioids in hospitals. If someone is involved in a car crash and has extensive damage to their body, they may be given around -the-clock opioids for up to a month. That medication is suddenly stopped, yet they do not have withdrawals. We also know as hypnotists, having helped thousands of clients to stop smoking, who may have tried for years unsuccessfully to quit, that they do so instantly with hypnosis. After a two-hour session with me, the majority of people walk out of the clinic and never smoke again with no dramatic withdrawal symptoms.

So is addiction physical or psychological?

To answer this, let us look further into the study of mind over matter. Here we must be careful not to fall into Descartes' (2017) dualism dichotomy of dividing the mind and body, which has frequently plagued the true investigation of the human condition since his theory more than 400 years ago. Unfortunately, allopathic medicine still teaches this philosophy today in medical schools all over the world. Descartes came to his damaging concept in an effort to separate science from spiritualism, but is not living a spiritual experience in itself part of the physical and mental process?

Let us look at the extraordinary feats the body can achieve by using the mind. Bruce Lee was one of the most skilled fighters that ever lived (Thomas, 1994). Although he died young from a heart attack, he mastered several martial arts disciplines and was able to execute them with stunning accuracy and endurance. His dedication and application of his mind to martial arts put him above the rest of the world in his field.

The legendary Dutchman Wim Hof, who, at the time of writing, holds 26 world records, is famous for training himself to withstand cold and freezing conditions, including climbing Mount Everest to 22,000 ft in nothing but shorts and shoes, and being immersed in ice for an hour and 52 minutes (Hof & De Jong, 2016). Dubbed 'the iceman', he has trained himself through breathing, endurance exercises and mental focus to extend the abilities of his body.

John Evans from Marpool in England is a world-record-holding strongman who balances cars on his head. He appeared on the American talk show hosted by Jay Leno in 1995 balancing a Mini on his head (Evans, 2009). He started as a hod carrier for bricks and then progressed to increasing the weights he could balance by focusing his mind when performing his feats.

The documentary *Running Raw* shows Janette Murray-Wakelin and her husband Alan Murray running 366 marathons, one per consecutive day, around Australia in 2013 (Florio, El Harris, & Mooney, 2017). At the time Janette was 63 and Alan 68. Fifteen years earlier Janette had been diagnosed with terminal cancer and given just six months to live, and Alan was overweight, a smoker and drank alcohol regularly. At that time they decided to change their lives, eat a raw vegetable-based diet and run daily. They focused on their health.

I often use metaphors about how the human body can do many things that might be beyond the ordinary. Metaphor is always entrancing as people follow the narrative and go inside to recreate the story in their imagination. I have a whole host of stories about amazing things that people have done that I use to demonstrate human potential but am indirectly suggesting that the client can have high potential too. It is what is known as the 'My friend John story' technique with both direct and indirect suggestion to get the message across to the client that they have far more potential than they were ever consciously aware of before they came into the therapy room.

What is equally important is that as a hypnotherapist you must have a strong underlying belief in what you are teaching your client. I am in awe of the people I have mentioned who achieved great feats, and spend time researching the ever-growing body of material that considers stretching human limits both physically and mentally. I bring that knowledge and enthusiasm into the therapy room and clients pick up on it both consciously and unconsciously in trance. I have seen thousands of people in my clinic stop addiction instantly, so my work has the presupposition that the client can do that as well.

As a therapist you have to be careful in using metaphor and comparatives that you do not put the client in a position where they are intimidated by your tales of people who achieve great feats. The addiction has damaged their self-esteem or perhaps they may never really have had good self-esteem. The aim of metaphor is to lift the client's expectations of themselves, not to make them feel less than others, which can easily happen accidentally.

(Tracie): You can just close your eyes Mary and relax back into the chair with your eyes resting (moving to a more receptive state of suggestion)...dreaming about some of the people I talked about (dreaming is associated with stretching the limits of reality)...**just ordinary people doing extraordinary things** (association of their potential with the client's potential)…people just like you and me (normalising achieving great things)…with all our human potential (affirming the client has great potential)…people who climb mountains…cross the arctic…run 366 marathons…lift cars…and a thousand other things (stretching the client's expectations)…**just like you being extraordinary here today stopping drinking** (ego-strengthening, affirming the client is stopping drinking today) …isn't it amazing what you can do when you put your mind to a task (presupposition the client can complete that task)…how focused you can be when you use your body to create marvellous experiences (suggestion to focus and change physiology)…yes you are a superhero (compounding ego-strengthening)…someone who is achieving an extraordinary experience (affirming the client is now stopping drinking)…**here today stop drinking** (direct suggestion)…time to come back into your body (re-association command)…**reclaiming your health, body, mind and being clean and sober** (direct suggestion for the client to take back their faculties and stop using substances)…smiling at your achievement opening your eyes and looking at me (contingent suggestion with having stopped drinking linked to opening of the eyes, driven by good Ki feelings).

As a hypnotherapist you offer many suggestions to the client but hypnotherapy should not be just a passive experience for them. The client needs to develop a mindset of self-efficacy about their ability to control their own situation, in and after they have left your clinic. This needs education, installation of those abilities, operation of those abilities and checking if those abilities are working. All of this needs to be constantly laced with ego-strengthening to repair the ego so it can once again moderate between the superego and the id.

Passive hypnotherapy is less effective than interactive hypnotherapy. Miller, Galanter, & Pribram (1960) introduced the use of the acronym TOTE (test – operate – test – exit). As you progressively, incrementally and relentlessly guide those changes within the client's mind through suggestion, you also need to check your work. See how the client is working. What are their comments, self-statements, body language and reactions to statements with which you test them? Choose your intervention carefully and operate the procedural change. Test again to see if the cognitive, behaviour and emotional change has taken place. If the change has taken place, you can then exit that part of the therapy; but if the change has not taken place, you must redesign an intervention and attempt the change again, until the client gets results.

Tracie:	OK Mary are you...**strong?**
Mary:	Yes.
Tracie:	Are you really really strong and **stronger than the alcohol?**
Mary:	Yes.
Tracie:	Have you **stopped drinking?**
Mary:	Yes.
Tracie:	Is life for you **without alcohol and substance abuse?**
Mary:	Yes.
Tracie:	**You don't want** to change your mind...do you?
Mary:	No.
Tracie:	So you really **don't want to drink** anymore?
Mary:	No.

People in the trance and somnambulistic state tend to respond literally with monosyllabic answers to questions, unless requested otherwise. When testing for cognitive and behavioural change, phrase questions, seek responses or ideomotor responses that require simple and binary responses. If you ask for in-depth reasoning, it requires analytical engagement of the brain and intellect, which runs the risk of bringing the client out of trance.

Catalepsy is a very good way to ratify trance in a client when combined with somnambulism. It builds confidence in the hypnotherapeutic process in the client's mind. Many hypnotists talk about catalepsy as a waxy muscular state where the limbs can be bent when placed into different positions, but it can also be rigidity of muscles. The clear sign is that the limbs will stay where you put them or suggest they should be positioned. It is also a great display to the client of mind over matter.

(Tracie): "Mary I noticed when I examined your hands earlier that they were shaking and you said that seems to be happening every day recently when you have not had a drink. I want you to focus on my right hand as I face opposite you (I extend my arm, and it is cataleptic, rigid, hand open and palms facing down)...**focus on my hand still as steel** (command for attention)...you know I would not normally hold my hand and arm like this in mid-air and perfectly still (suggestion for something being an extraordinary experience)...with my hand that's left I'm going to place your hand that is left the same (confusion technique to prepare the client for suggestion because they go into transderivational search to make sense of my suggestion, suggestion to model the stillness of my hand)...**watch your hand** (ratification of modelling)...**focus on your hand** (suggestion for awareness of physical change)... isn't it interesting that it is now so still too (I gently stroke her hand on the top and bottom with my free hand)...isn't your body clever what it can do (acknowledgment the client can change their physiology)...**nerves of steel** (suggestion for stillness of the hand, suggestion for ego-strengthening)...focusing on your hand you can understand the power of your unconscious mind (causal link, suggestion for awareness of unconscious potential)...aren't you amazing (ego-strengthening)...**focus on the hand** (suggestion for awareness of physical change)...**nerves of steel** (suggestion for stillness of the hand, suggestion for ego-strengthening)...see how fast your body can change with the power of your mind (suggestion for fast physical change)...it stopped your hand shaking just as (ratification of the efficacy of hypnotic suggestion, moving the physical change into the past tense)...**you stop drinking today** (direct suggestion).

When I work with someone, I am animated. I am in full belief that the work will help them and I am excited about their potential progress, which comes across to the client. Even if the client has their eyes closed, I still make the appropriate facial expressions that are associated with a specific suggestion. I also use the body language associated with that suggestion. Your body is hard-wired to modulate sound according to the message you are delivering. If you attempt to deliver suggestions in a monotone, boring, unanimated voice, the client's unconscious will read you as insincere, uninterested and ignore the suggestion. Effective hypnotists have dramatic delivery to create cognitive overload in the client's mind and render them suggestive.

Greenberg (1977) edited a book about hypnodrama. It was the use of hypnosis in group therapy and the psychoimaginary acting out of suggested scenarios. While this may help remodel the unconscious topography, physically acting out dramatic possibilities also helps re-pattern neurophysiology. During a session I will act out a scenario physically with a client. I will also get them acting out the scenarios and ideas we want them to embrace. When you introduce new scenarios and ideas, they are to override old thought patterns and behaviours.

(Tracie): So now Mary you can use that hand of steel (building on previous learning experience)...that steady happy hand you have been using (ratification that she has mastered mind over matter)...**a hand of steel saying stop drinking alcohol** (association of the past success of catalepsy with the ability to decide to stop drinking, contingent suggestion)...put out that hand that's right right in front of you (confusion, direct suggestion)... straight out in front of you just like I'm doing (direct suggestion, modelling)...**making the stop sign now strong as steel** (direct suggestion associated with the strong ability to reject alcohol)... isn't that powerful (interrogative suggestion)...you're going to be using that stop sign for the rest of your life giving clear indications you reject alcohol (future pacing)...**look how strong that hand is now** (Ve validation of her ability to reject alcohol)...look how strong you are now (dissociated ratification of how strongly she can say no to alcohol)...when you encounter alcohol (suggestion for all circumstances)...you can gently raise your hand in the stop sign as you reject the drink 'No thank you not for me' (contingent suggestion, situational suggestion)...**Wow how clear of mind and strong you look** (clarifying cognitive thought pattern, personal acknowledgment of her ability to reject alcohol, external acknowledgment of her ability to reject alcohol, fractionation of her ability by using 'Wow').

Delivery of suggestions for a pattern interrupter mechanism delivered by hypnosis has been used traditionally throughout time. It works in so many ways. In this case it is helping Mary install a chain reaction that occurs every time she comes into contact with alcohol. Coming into contact with alcohol is the trigger, regardless of where, when, how or why that might be.

As we go through the session, each time we install a cognitive and behavioural change, I am acknowledging the change and ego-strengthening Mary so she feels she is making the change happen. Change-of-thought pattern and behaviour is not enough to cement that change as the client must also be driven by internal kinaesthetic good feelings.

We do not change our thoughts and behaviours because it is analytically the most logical thing to do, but because it is emotionally gratifying for us. Emotions always trump logic in or out of hypnosis. Any good salesperson will tell you we buy emotionally and then find ways to back up our purchase with logic. Emotions are our most powerful and fastest drivers and responses. We are human beings, not computers, and the addict will only stop addiction when an emotional option is presented to them that makes them feel better than their substance of abuse, because addiction is driven by the id and is a primitive reward and avoidance mechanism. Therapists must incite good feelings in the client around being clean and sober.

The client has already experienced many pattern interrupters in their life when you start working with them. The pattern interrupters must be simple, comprehensible, strong, primitive, unambiguous and universal. The first pattern interrupter all children learn is a parent saying "No!", the second is "Stop it", and if a parent does not install those at an early age, that child will have a poor sense of boundaries and is likely to have social problems. By associating your pattern interrupter with those early learning messages, you regress the client, lowering their conscious critical defences to change, rendering them more suggestible.

As a therapist you are re-parenting the client. While you may induce a sense of friendship to lower defences, the demarcation of your role must be clear in that you are the guide leading the way to safety. The client has within their unconscious mind all those memory trances of the "No" and the "Stop it" and they have been programmed to obey those commands, so you simply have to tap into what behaviours already exist and utilise them to help the client stop taking the substance.

Tracie: *It is today isn't it Mary that you stop drinking alcohol (interrogative double bind, all the work she has done so far stops her from disagreeing without major discomfort)? It is today here now isn't it you take back your sobriety Mary (interrogative direct suggestion for instant sobriety)? Mary you can't help but feel this is your time your time your time to become clean and sober, can you (confusion, cognitive overload, working Ki good feeling driver for clean and sober)? Isn't that right Mary?*

Mary: *Yes.*

Tracie: *For you alcohol is dangerous and always will be. It's not worked for you. It steals from your life and well-being. Since you have experienced addiction in your life then no addictive substances have any place in your future. So Step 2 is Stop Taking the Substance. And you are learning it so well. It is so easy. Step 1 is Stay Out of Denial. Your en garde part operates 24/7/365 operating for the rest of your life. When you come into contact with alcohol in any way your en garde part sounds the alarm and you automatically move to Step 2 Stop Taking the Substance. You have a right to live clean and sober. Being clean and sober is your life now.*

Step 2 – Stop Taking the Substance: Future-paced rehearsal for stop mechanism for drugs and alcohol intentions

1. Step 2 installs a Pavlovian response "The Stop Mechanism".
2. The stop mechanism is a pattern interrupter.
3. The sounding of the alarm by the en garde part (Vi, Ai, Ki) initiates the cue for the pattern interrupter to reject addictive substances and initiate rejecting actions (Ke, Ae, Ae).
4. People are trained by their parents at an early age to operate

stopping behaviours. They already have parallel experiences in their lives when they use the stop mechanism; it is a familiar mechanism to them and easy for them to repeat.

5. In building in the stop mechanism it is important to build it in so it activates a chain link process with step 1 leading to step 2 automatically.

6. The key to building the neural pathways for the series of associated experiences is repetition.

Step 2 – Stop Taking the Substance: Future-paced rehearsal for stop mechanism for drugs and alcohol trance script

(Tracie): I wonder if you might imagine Mary with your eyes closed a moment (positive hallucination)…seeing yourself up inside your head (high visual field imagery)…**you're singing dancing clean and sober** (Vi+ Ai+ Ki+)…how happy do you look (transderivational search, interrogative suggestion, affirmation of the clean and sober state)…how great do you feel (transderivational search, interrogative suggestion for well-being, Ki+, ratification of sobriety)…what do you say inside your head (transderivational search, interrogative suggestion for competent internal dialog for sobriety)…**I am clean and sober** (affirmation of sobriety, present and future pacing)…with every breath it grows stronger (pacing increasing sobriety, direct suggestion for sobriety, contingent suggestion to breathing)…you are so clear in all of your mind when you encounter drugs or alcohol (unconscious programming for cognitive awareness)…**you hear I am clean and sober** (auditory hallucination, present tense certainty, future pace)… your en garde part is always on duty 24/7/365 for the rest of your life (superego programming)…you fall in love with yourself as clean and sober (ego-strengthening)…**more and more and more with each and every breath** (fractionation linked to contingent suggestion for breathing, Pavlovian response, catch-all generalisation)…it feels good to **be…clean and sober** (ratification of Ki+

to sobriety)...having control of your life (suggestion for sobriety as a way of life, ego-strengthening)...**every day you recommit to being clean and sober** (suggestion for daily behavioural reinstallation program)...you are strong in your refusal of drugs and alcohol (ego-strengthening around refusal behaviour)...you are certain those addictive substances are never for you (strengthening commitment to sobriety)...what other people do is their business (suggestion for independent behaviour)...**and you do clean and sober again and again and again** (fractionation)... I wonder how different your life will be (transderivational search, interrogative suggestion for change) and as your body rests safe (pacing safety)...your mind can listen to each and every word I say (post-hypnotic suggestion for paying attention to suggestions)...**my words becoming your words** (transference)...you know more than you know you know and you know I know you know that (transderivational search, confusion, trance deepener)...with each breath (preparation for suggestion to be linked to breathing)...**you know automatically how to be clean and sober** (contingent suggestion, Pavlovian response)...and whenever you come in contact with alcohol or drugs (superego installation and fractionation)...you can hear and see the word (causal cognitive awareness Vi, Ai)...**STOP! inside your mind** (positive hallucination)...**saying no thank you I'm clean and sober** (post-hypnotic suggestion for pattern interrupter)... and you feel good (triggering Ki+) taking three deep breaths... One...Two...Three...**saying no thank you I'm clean and sober** (automatic Ke, Ae, Ge responses to the presence of addictive substances)...and you feel so strong in your identity of being clean and sober (ego-strengthening, Ki+)...**remember automatically clean and sober with each and every breath** (contingent suggestion and post-hypnotic suggestion)...it's good to be you (ego-strengthening)...**it's good to have control of your life isn't it** (transderivational search, interrogative suggestion, future pacing sobriety)...and when you come back to the room you can bring all those good thoughts and feelings with you…**and most of all you can be proud of your achievement** (transference of control)…you are the queen of clean and sober…hey is that a crown on your head.

Mary stopped drinking immediately and remained clean and sober for six weeks. The seventh weekend she spent with her Irish relatives who drank profusely and she got drunk on the Saturday night. When I saw her again she was mortified about her relapse but she immediately picked herself up and never drank alcohol again during the ensuing months.

We worked on her interviewing skills and she got a job she liked. After that, I put her on a weight loss program and she became healthier and far more proud about how she looked. At Christmas I got a text from her, thanking me for my help and saying that her life had totally changed and she was having a great time clean and sober, to which I replied:

"Thank you for your kind words and remember anything is possible ☺"

Medications used in stopping extreme abuse

In some cases, addiction is so intense, long-standing and accompanied by psychological disturbance that the client may need extra help to stop the addiction immediately. A clinician is faced with offering the client drugs of another kind such as methadone, sedatives, anxiolytics or anti-depressants or getting them to take medications that block the effects of the addictive substances. Non-medical professionals need to co-ordinate with family doctors or addiction specialists. These drugs may be marketed under other names in different countries or other drugs may be used off-label.

However, there is a caveat here in that doctors using them, along with pharmaceutical companies that give benefits to medics for prescribing them, can talk them up. Burlison (2016) sees pushing medications like this as being the ultimate answer to addiction, at times disparaging the non-medication route to sobriety as being unscientific. For some patients, however, such drugs do not work out as a suitable solution and nor can they change addictive behaviours by themselves.

My preference in working with people is to reduce medications to a minimum so the client is forced to use their brain and body to produce self-satisfying experiences. I often come up against other clinicians involved who are of different opinions and I will explain my approach at lengths, lobbying the no-or-low drug approaches. The drugs I will lobby for in extreme addiction are substance abuse blockers for a limited period of weeks only. I have only ever recommended them four times out of the thousands of patients I have treated, because they were at serious risk of liver or kidney failure, paraesthesia or cardiac arrest, due to their addiction.

Antabuse (Disulfiram) is an alcohol deterrent that makes the client feel sick and nauseous after being in contact with alcohol. The body reacts so strongly when this drug is administered that mere contact with an alcohol-based aftershave or alcohol-based medical swab can initiate a violent physical reaction. The US Department of Health and Human Services (2013) tells us that this was the first addiction withdrawal medication of its type approved by the Food and Drug Administration (FDA), yet it has not become a standard treatment.

Many alcoholics worry about the effects of the DTs (Delirium tremens) when alcohol is stopped suddenly. The alcoholic goes into confusion, the body shakes and delirium manifests. Clients may even believe to stop alcohol suddenly is physically dangerous, which it is not with the help of hypnosis, but psychologically it can lead to panic and even suicidal thoughts. So in extreme cases, having someone watch the alcoholic when they are initially stopping the behaviour is a good idea. Alcoholism is a state-dependent behaviour and as hypnotherapists we are creating a new state-dependent behaviour of being clean and sober.

Methadone is a synthetic opioid medication used in heroin withdrawal. My clinical experience is that this medication causes more problems for the addict because it is transference of addiction. For those of you who are medically trained, you have been sold the myth that it is an easier step to reduce opioid addiction, but in reality, the addict does not stop their addictive behaviour. Again I come back to the FDA's (US Food and Drug Administration, 2013) warning that long-term use leads to addiction; however, in my opinion, short-term use simply transfers addiction.

Naltrexone is an opioid antagonist that blocks opioid receptors and kills the addict's high. It is used in the management of alcohol and opioid addiction. It should not be confused with **naloxone** which is administered in hospitals to treat overdoses in heroin addicts who often wake up annoyed that they are no longer high. Naltrexone is expensive as a slow release injection and has few effects on reducing the craving of the substance of abuse. Bart (2012) stated that the use of this drug increases long-term outcomes for withdrawing addicts but fails to mention the millions of users who have stopped addiction without chemical assistance.

Buprenorphine is a synthetic opioid and antagonist used as a heroin substitute and is often used in withdrawal programs from heroin and methadone (2 types Sub Oxone Sublingual Film, Subutex Sublingual Tablets). It is at times used in combination with Naltrexone. It is rated as being as effective as methadone for heroin withdrawal and used in methadone withdrawal programs. Schaller (2006) suggested it was a magical medication that made addiction withdrawal painless for 30 days to 30 years.

Major problems with addicts trying to override the antagonistic effects of medications have, however, been reported, with addicts having taken large amounts of heroin to counteract the effect, leading to death by overdose.

One of the great fears of clinicians around withdrawal is the possible occurrence of seizures due to various detoxification shock complications. For this reason, some emergency psychiatric wards will administer doses of benzodiazepine, 20 milligrams every two hours. This practice is futile as it does not address the addiction, and, in my experience, constant hypnosis and large doses of magnesium or calming herbs can achieve equally as good results.

The brutality of withdrawal cannot be avoided in some extreme addiction cases. Constant hypnosis and post-hypnotic suggestion reduces those ill effects and, in some cases, eliminates them. The ill effects of withdrawal typically peak at between 48-72 hours, although it can take up to 28 days for the body to begin to produce good levels of endorphins, dopamine and serotonin all by itself. It is rarely solely a physical brutality but also a psychobiological one. There is a case for a progressive withdrawal method being used with heroin addicts by reducing doses and frequency of use in some cases. However, it is important to remember that withdrawal from all addiction lays bare underlying physical and psychological pathologies that must be managed and dealt with swiftly to prevent the temptation of a relapse.

Bandura, A. (1997). *Self-efficacy: The exercise of control.* New York, NY: W. H. Freeman.

Bart, G. (2012). Maintenance medication for opiate addiction: The foundation of recovery. *Journal of Addictive Diseases, 31*(3), 207–225. doi:10.1080/10550887.2012.694598

Burlison, L. (2016). *A prescription for alcoholics: Medications for alcoholism.* New York, NY: Addiction Publishing.

Descartes, R. (2017). *The collected works of René Descartes* [Kindle edition]. Retrieved from http://www.amazon.com

Dick, D. M., & Agrawal, A. (2008). The genetics of alcohol and other drug dependence. *Alcohol, Research and Health, 31*(2), 111–118.

Evans, J. (2009, May 8). *John Evans appearing on the TV show "Tonight Show with Jay Leno"* [Video file]. Retrieved from https://www.youtube.com/watch?v=fAeNgVlcxtk

Florio, J., El-Harris, F. (Producers), & Mooney, M.-J. (Director). (2017). *Raw: The documentary* [Motion picture]. Sydney, Australia: Old School Productions.

Frank, J .W., Moore, R. S., & Ames, G. M. (2000). Historical and cultural roots of drinking problems among American Indians. *American Journal of Public Health, 90*(3), 344–351.

Greenberg, I. R. (1977). *Group hypnotherapy and hypnodrama.* Lanham, Maryland: Burnham.

Hof, W., & De Jong, K. (2016). *The way of the iceman: How Wim Hof creates radiant longterm health using the science and secrets of breath control, cold training and commitment* [Kindle version]. Retrieved from http://www.amazon.com

Miller, G. A., Galanter, E., & Pribram, K. H. (1960). *Plans and the structure of behaviour*. Eastford, CT: Martino Fine Books.

Rohsenow, D. J. (1983). Drinking habits and expectancies about alcohol effects for self versus others. *Journal of Consulting and Clinical Psychology, 51*(5), 752–756.

Thomas, B. (1994). *Bruce Lee: Fighting spirit*. Berkeley, CA: Blue Snake Books.

Schaller, J. (2006). *Suboxone: Take back your life from pain medications*. Tampa, FL: Hope Academic Press.

U. S. Department of Health and Human Services. (2013). *Incorporating alcohol pharmacotherapies into medical practice*. (TIP 49). Retrieved from http://store.samhsa.gov/shin/content//SMA13-4380/SMA13-4380.pdf

U. S. Food and Drug Administration. (2013). *Information for healthcare professionals methadone hydrochloride*. Retrieved from https://www.fda.gov/Drugs/DrugSafety/PostmarketDrugSafetyInformationforPatientsandProviders/ucm142841.htm

World Health Organization. (2014). *Global status report on alcohol and health*. Geneva, Switzerland: Author.

7 *Do Something Different*

The medical establishment has classified addiction as a disease. The *DSM-5* states various categories of addiction under substance use disorders in the classification of diseases, medicalising addiction (American Psychiatric Association, 2013). The *ICD 11* also proposes to classify addiction as inherently a disease (First, Reed, Hyman, & Saxena, 2015). From a disease model, we are not talking about infection or inherited or congenital defects or genetic differences but simply a deviation from biological homeostasis and normal functioning.

For funding and medical insurance purposes, the medicalising of addiction works to access government and private medical insurance coverage for treatment of addiction when people cannot afford private treatment. This, however, confuses the issue of what addiction might be and in a previous chapter I have discussed whether addiction is physical or mental.

This is further complicated by two more factors. Firstly, when we see clients to stop addiction, they may be suffering from physiological and psychological problems that have arisen due to the side effects of the substance abuse. Secondly, we can see clients whose physical, psychological and social problems made them more susceptible to addictive behaviours.

For most people, withdrawal symptoms from substance abuse are short-lived, although many addicts believe they will last a long time. For some people, the damage the substance has done to their physiology and mental state means they could suffer long-term damage and remain dysfunctional.

Let us for a moment think about addicts without hearing anything they are saying. Just think about the addicts you know and see in your mind what they do. What you will see is a series of repetitive actions and behaviours that may be circumstances-based or not. Clients are doing the same thing over and over and over again, even if that is at varied intervals. As a clinician, you must watch what your client does because what they tell you is often unreliable. When you are checking for changes in your clients, you can watch their body and face language change as they make cognitive and behaviour changes.

Simon: *I've been doing the same things for the last two years, only getting worse. When my wife left me for another bloke I was gutted. We'd just bought a house, had good jobs, money in the bank and I thought we were all right together. I just didn't see it coming. My doctor put me on two types of anti-depressants, then anti-anxiety meds and sleeping pills, then Lithium because he said I was bi-polar. I've ended up suicidal. Now he wants me to see a specialist to have ECT [electro-convulsive therapy]. In the last two years I've lost my job and the house, can't work, can't think straight and it's one pill after another.*

Tracie: *I am so on your side Simon. I'm hearing every-thing you are saying and listening. I'm really glad your parents are helping you by letting you live at their house. That they are doing that is wonderful and it goes part way to restoring your faith in human nature. What has stood out to me however is your statements: 'I've been doing the same things for the last two years only get-ting worse', and 'I can't think straight and it's one*

pill after another'. I think you have worked out
for yourself that things as they are at the mo-
ment aren't working for you.

Simon: *My mother is saying I have to do what the family*
doctor says and my father says he's a quack and
turning me into a zombie.

Wolinsky & Ryan (1991) in their book *Trances People Live* talk about how we move from one trance to another in our lives. We also recreate earlier trances where we were traumatised and relive them again and again, sometimes for years, decades or life, until something breaks that trance. People in addictive trances have belief systems that support that constant, repetitive behaviour of addiction. They are stuck in a behavioural loop. The looped behaviours do not permit them to develop new belief systems, thoughts and behaviours, so they are stuck in this endless cycle of continually going back to the substance of abuse.

While the addictive looped behaviours have become self-perpetuating, the belief system that supports them has been originally fed by trauma, social conditioning, social norms, sub-culture norms, advice from others, living life according to other people's demands, and most of all, the fear of change. Not only does the client fear behavioural change but also physical change.

Griffith & Griffith (1994) in their book *The Body Speaks* talk about how physical symptoms can frequently be driven by psychodynamic conflict and common social understanding, causing psychosomatic conditions. Layered onto that is the etiological understanding of language, how disease is understood by the patient, and the training and understanding of suffering that the clinician brings to the situation.

As hypnotherapists our philosophy and linguistic terminology, semantics and pragmatics shape our clinical outcomes because we are a suggestive discipline. If we tell the client they would find it difficult to change and do something else other than addiction, the client will more than likely adopt that suggestion as a self-fulfilling prophecy. On the other hand, if we suggest to our clients that change is possible, imminent and well within their capacity, they will begin to live that trance and experience no or fewer withdrawal symptoms.

(Tracie): You know Simon I'm impressed with your progress in the session (ratification of change, ego-strengthening)...I agree with you these medications are making you worse (truism, building therapeutic alliance) what are you learning today (re-enforcing learning by reviewing what has been learned)...**Step 1 Stay Out of Denial** (post-hypnotic suggestion)...always being aware of maintaining your life as clean and sober (general time frame intrahypnotic and post-hypnotic suggestion) ...sobriety is for you (single option suggestion)...**having your en garde part on duty 24/7/365** (post-hypnotic suggestion)...when it comes into contact with substances that are not right for you it sounds the alarm (contingent suggestion)...**you move immediately to Step 2 Stop Taking the Substance** (post-hypnotic suggestion)...since you're on prescription drugs we are going to have you withdraw from them slowly and progressively under a physician (time framing, future pacing, giving him a sense of having more advocates)... **you are moving to Step 3 Do Something Different** (post-hypnotic suggestion)...you came here today for a big change in your life Simon so that what is we are going to do aren't we (restating the client's intention, interrogative suggestion, enlarging the goal, making it more compelling, future pacing success).

Simon: Yes.

Tracie: And you don't want anything less, do you?

Simon: No.

Tracie: *And you won't let anyone take that change away*
           from you, will you?

Simon: *No.*

Rothschild (2000) in her book *The Body Remembers* talks about how people carry their past traumatic memories around in their body, which can be triggered by a purposeful suggestion or accidental stimuli. We can see this to be true in therapy when clients who have experienced sexual abuse may develop frigidity or can develop abreactions when touched. It can also be observed when we view the body language of unconfident people who suffered mental abuse as children. Segerstrom & Miller (2004) reviewed 300 studies that showed people suffer a compromised immune system when exposed to stress.

Further evidence that suggestion and mental experience cause physiological change can be seen when we look at Lambert's (1996) study of increased post-operative recovery from surgery in children who received hypnosis. The Hilgards (Hilgard & Hilgard, 1994) published extensive research in the exploration of using hypnosis to effect pain control. Yapko (2001) wrote about how he uses hypnosis to relieve depression with an indirect Ericksonian approach.

It is not therefore a stretch of the imagination that as hypnotherapists we can, through suggestions, therapeutically change the client's physiology. When I work with addicts, most of them do not experience or experience considerably reduced withdrawal symptoms due to the alteration of belief, expectation, physiological experience, sub-modality changes and self-suggestion in the first session.

Brown (1994) describes the move towards a psychobiological model of dissociation, which is a sense of leaving the body, and also the person is no longer operating via their central, main personality. So during mental pathology, the person may be acting out via sub-routines of an alternative personality, which splits from the central personality, often quoted as being due to early childhood trauma. We can consider, however, that dissociation is a natural defence mechanism that can happen at any time of life when faced with trauma and difficult circumstances. Here, of course, we must be careful not to run into the Cartesian separation of mind and body.

As a naturopath, I see all substance addiction as a form of dissociation from the central personality and body. The addictive personality has taken centre stage and seeks to protect itself against being deposed. As both a physical and mental therapist, my philosophy is that we have to heal both together so that physical and mental functions restore synchronicity. They are never separate and this is best served by getting the client to re-integrate back into their body. A healthy, central, core self-preserving personality looks after both the homeostasis of the body and subjugates the id's greed for the substance of abuse. To attempt to heal the mind without healing the body is like trying to travel on the motorway without a functional vehicle.

Tracie: You know I'm a naturopath Simon...right?

Simon: Yes.

Tracie: And you know naturopaths are obsessed with health...don't you?

Simon: Yes.

Tracie: So it follows that in coming to see me you are going to become pretty obsessed with your own health too...doesn't it?

Simon: Yes.

Tracie: How obsessed?

Simon: Very?

Tracie:	How obsessed?
Simon:	A lot?
Tracie:	How obsessed?
Simon:	Extremely.
Tracie:	When?
Simon:	Now.

Creating a clean and sober body trance script

(Tracie): Close your eyes and focus inside focusing on your body (direct suggestion to pay attention to the physical self)...take care of Simon (direct suggestion to take responsibility and putting the central core personality centre stage)...for a long time you have left your body (truism)...**it's time to step back inside your body** (direct suggestion for physical re-integration)...no time to waste time is a ticking (suggestion for expedient action)... feel your toes (suggestion for physical sensory awareness)...your hands...nose...ears...legs...**each and every part of your body** (suggestion for full physical sensory awareness)...it's down to you now (accountability, transference of the ability to recover physically)...it's your chariot you travel through life in (accountability, ego-strengthening by raising the status of the body to a chariot, eliciting the warrior self archetype)...it's getting well (intrahypnotic suggestion)...**it's about taking care of your body again always** (indirect suggestion, allowing for reinstatement of looking after himself physically, carrying the therapeutic presupposition of being clean and sober, future pacing)... for you being drug free gives you back your strength (association between being drug free and strength)...of course you remember how to be drug free and strong don't you (regression, memory recall, interrogative suggestion for drug withdrawal)... **with every breath you are regaining control over your body** (contingent suggestion)...your health and sanity now (restating client's goals helps them focus on them)...peace by peace by peace by peace (vocal intonation for a peaceful state, phonological ambiguity, chunking by allowing the client to gradually withdraw from the drugs)...**all the way back in your body** (direct suggestion for re-integration)...that's right (pacing, verification of re-integration)...a body that is now becoming healthy (ratification of progress)...**you're creating your clean and sober body** (direct suggestion)...so so good (suggestion for positive internal kinaesthetic feelings, fractionation)...smiling and looking at me (indirect suggestion for somnambulism and opening the eyes, association of good feelings linked to the work the client is doing).

In his book *Pathways to Reality*, Lovern (1991) demonstrates the Ericksonian style of hypno-psychotherapy when working with people recovering from chemical dependency. It is a style of working with the client in conversational therapy in various levels of the hypnotic state but, most importantly, working psychotherapeutically.

Hull (2002), who was largely responsible for initiating the scientific approach to studying hypnotic phenomena, and was Milton Erickson's tutor, favoured the direct suggestion delivery. He believed the hypnotist was the main protagonist and that the hypnosis was a heightened state of suggestion.

As I was trained as an Ericksonian hypno-psychotherapist, as a traditional hypnotherapist and in many styles of hypnosis and therapy, I move between the two major modes with clients as I provoke change in the client's psychodynamic functioning.

There are times when interacting with your client that you may want to elicit more than just simple monosyllabic responses or ideomotor responses. When working with the client somnambulistically, you may want to change your client to conversational hypnosis because you want to check the evidence of their mental change. We do not live in our client's head or know their thoughts, so we have to get them to verbalise what they are thinking and experiencing.

Tracie: So Simon we talked about you slowly coming off these medications. It's interesting that you never had any sign of being bipolar or having had depression before your wife left you. You also reported never having had a manic episode. All the evidence then points to you having experienced trauma and shock when your wife left you and that suggests that the decline in your mental health was due to your circumstances. I'm going to recommend another family doctor to you who will take you off one medication per month until you are taking none. What do you think?

Simon: My dad says the same thing as you but my family doctor tells him he is wrong. I just want my life back. I want to be how I was before. I used to be so happy. I want to be able to think. I want a job. I want to feel well again and get better.

Tracie: You are going in the right direction now. Piece by piece you will regain your thinking and your mind's clarity as you follow everything I ask you to do. What you have started to do here today will change your life. We are working on what you will be doing rather than relying on drugs. This of course is what you used to do so it is not at all alien to you and is in fact very familiar. So how are you changing here now today?

Simon: I'm taking responsibility to make my life good again. I'm not going to let that doctor drug me anymore. I'm going to listen to my dad and do what he says and do what you say and what the new family doctor you recommended says.

The client comes to us in the substance-taking state, however they got there, and we need to help them break that trance and learn to do things differently. What we need to install is another trance state connected with happiness, health and well-being. Do we always need to know every detail about what they will do? – No. Do we need to guide them in the direction we want them to go? – Yes.

Step 3 – Do Something Different intentions

1. The old trance of taking drugs and alcohol was a repetition which ended in the same result of taking the substance.
2. Part of the first three steps of recovery is to get the client motivated to do other things than the addictive behaviour. This requires both cognitive discussion and trance installation.
3. Do not obviously choose the different behaviour that the client will do, as it may give rise to resistance.
4. Elicit from the client what might be good for them.
5. Indirect suggestion can be woven into conversation to guide the client to live a healthier life and enact healthier behaviours.
6. Be clear with the client that they need to have good boundaries to allow the new behaviours to be an everyday and hourly occurrence.

Step 3 – Do Something Different trance script
(Tracie): Simon close your eyes and think for a moment think about the repetition of your previous addictive behaviour (regression)…just stand back in your mind and see how you seemed to have been doing the same thing again and again without thinking (dissociation, remote viewing)…isn't it fascinating the things we did without paying attention (transderivational search, suggestion for self-analysis, time shift)…**you can have other choices** (permissive suggestion for alternative behaviours)…nothing is forever as you change time the way you want

it to be (time distortion, suggestion for change) you will have new things you do rather than taking that substance in future (post-hypnotic suggestion for new behaviour options)…you can wonder what you will do instead (transderivational search, suggestion for generating new options)…perhaps you could go for a jog (permissive suggestion for exercise)…**how will you create your health** (transderivational search, interrogative suggestion for better health awareness)…what creative and constructive positive things will you do (transderivational search, interrogative suggestion)…**making a better life for you and others** (direct suggestion, ego-strengthening, appealing to the super-ego)…having so many options (truism)…such a better life (unconsciously rearranging the value system)…again and again and again and again (suggestion for future-paced repetition of the new trance)…**you will make better clean and sober choices** (direct suggestion)…automatically choosing clean and sober behaviours (direct suggestion)…**automatically with each and every breath you refuse that substance and choose your clean and sober behaviours with pleasure** (contingent suggestion, direct suggestion, suggestion for Pavlovian response, behaviour prohibition, illusion of choice).

I am generally a brief therapist. Clients come to see me because they want fast, reliable results which fit into their busy lives or they wish to remedy their situation speedily. Rosen (1991) tells us that Erickson talked about tasking clients by giving them homework to do in between sessions, which did two things. Firstly Erickson was testing them for compliance and secondly he was setting them up for success. My clients know in advance from my patient guide and the contract they sign that they will be given homework and will be expected to complete those tasks in between sessions. If a client persistently does not follow that tasking, I explain to them I cannot help them as they appear to be not truly invested in therapy.

In tasking clients, however, we must be mindful of the level of brain damage caused by the addictions. Both recreational and prescription drugs can cause damage to structures of the brain and create hormonal dysregulation. Torvik, Lindboe, & Rogde (1982) found on examination of hundreds of cadavers of alcoholics the presence of brain lesions and lower brain weight in comparison with a control group. Berman, O'Neill, Fears, Bartzokis, & London (2008) found through reviewing the brain MRIs of methamphetamine users that imaging displayed lower cortical grey matter volume and higher striatal volume compared to control subjects. We can also see dysmenorrhoea in female patients who use opioids and amphetamines. Santen, Sofsky, Bilic & Lippert (1975), in reviewing cases of heroin addicts, found menstrual irregularities both during opioid use and afterwards.

Hypnotherapy in the first session is designed to help the client with immediate cessation of the addiction. Therapy, however, must always be universal in that the therapist is motivating the client to live clean and sober on a day-to-day basis. At the end of the first session I always make a recording with the client that they can take away with them and use at home daily anything from three to seven times a day depending on the severity of the addiction. To simply rely on therapy within the therapy session is generally insufficient to stop addiction as the client must be rehearsed daily in a different way of living their life. This is cemented by engaging the client in hypnosis and suggestion outside the therapy sessions.

Stop substance abuse

Take-home first session 10 minutes intentions

The largest part of therapy takes place outside the therapy room through the client operating new behaviours and reinforcing those cognitive processes, behaviours and emotions.

1. We know from behavioural economics that the more some-

one repeats cognitions and behaviours, the more automatic they become.

2. It is important that the client is taking control of their own situation, increasing self-efficacy and self-agency.

3. Daily repetition through hypnosis, outside therapy sessions, creates change faster.

4. It is important for you, the therapist, to make it clear to the client that part of the treatment is to follow those daily hypnotic tasks and any other tasking you set for them.

5. You record Steps 1, 2 and 3 in the first session to initially aid them in ceasing the addictive behaviour that they then take away with them. At the beginning of the recording, you use a trance induction and at the end, a coming-out-of-trance routine. I tend to use a progressive relaxation routine because it takes clients out of the fight or flight response. The client listens to this recording with stereo headphones a minimum of three times a day but may use it more times a day, plus whenever they may need. Record this on their telephone as it will go with them wherever they go.

Stop substance abuse – Take-home recording

(Tracie): OK Simon it's your special time (separating trance time from ordinary conscious functioning)…find yourself a space in your mind where you will be undisturbed (focusing the client's mind)…be still (stillness induces a deeper trance state)…**with your eyes closed and going inside into a trance** (direct command to going deeper into a trance)… and as your body rests safe (pacing)…your mind can listen to each and every word I say (unconscious instructions)…**my words becoming your words** (transference)…you know more than you know you know and you know I know you know that (confusion, transderivational search – trance deepener)…with each breath…**you know automatically how to be clean and sober** (contingent suggestion)… and whenever you come in contact with alcohol or drugs (contingent suggestion, activating step 1)…you can hear and see the word (causal cognitive awareness)…**STOP! inside your mind** (positive hallucination)…**saying no thank you I'm clean and sober** (post-hypnotic suggestion, Pavlovian response)…and you feel good (triggering Ki good feelings) taking three deep breaths…**One**……. **Two**…….**Three**………**saying no thank you I'm clean and sober** (contingent suggestion, Pavlovian response, action Step 2)…and you feel so strong in your identity of being clean and sober (ego strengthening Ki+)…**remember automatically clean and sober with each and every breath** (contingent suggestion and post-hypnotic)…it's good to be you (ego strengthening)…**it's good to have control of your life isn't it** (transderivational search, future pacing sobriety)… and whenever you come in contact with alcohol or drugs (activating step 1)…you can hear and see the word (suggestion sensory awareness, installing Palovian response)…**STOP! inside your mind** (positive hallucination. Activating step 2)… **saying no thank you I'm clean and sober** (post-hypnotic suggestion, Pavlovian response)…and you feel good (triggering Ki good feelings) taking three deep breaths…**One**……**Two**……**Three**… **saying no thank you I'm clean and sober** (contingent suggestion, Pavlovian response)…and when you come back to the room you can bring all those good thoughts and feelings with you (post-hypnotic suggestion)…**and most of all you can be proud of your achievement…so…so proud** (transference of power to the client).

As a naturopath, I am also involved in healing the client's body as well as their mind. They are given instructions of things I wish them to do in order to become more healthy. The body of an addict is not in a state of homeostasis, gut dysbiosis is generally present, they are often nutritionally depleted, may have toxic poisoning, and there is often a hormonal and immunological dysregulation. If you are not medically qualified I suggest you also refer the client to a registered naturopath for support.

Tracie: You know Simon I'm going to give you lots of homework don't you?

Simon: Yes Tracie...my friend who has been here before told me you would.

Tracie: And you know we are stacking all the odds in your favour don't you?

Simon: I've got that impression.

Tracie: And did your friend get what he wanted from coming to see me?

Simon: He has never smoked a cigarette since.

Tracie: And you did fantastic today. You can be really proud of yourself. You will do very well Simon very well indeed.

Homework list:

- Listen to your recording 3 × a day and any other time you may need when in private with your headphones on (If the addiction is severe, move to 4 × a day and any other time you may need)
- No non-essential medications
- 2 litres of water a day
- Begin exercise three times a week
- Move towards a plant-based diet (detox and recovery is faster)
- No added sugar or preservatives, including MSG
- No processed junk food
- No tobacco (in severe opioid addiction this may have to be progressive)
- No caffeine
- No alcohol
- No drugs (or reduction in cases of prescription

medication – progressive detoxification, in conjunction
with family doctor)
- Multivitamins daily with minerals
- B complex daily
- Vitamin C 500mgs 2 × a day or higher dose through
liposomal ingestion
- Probiotics 2 × a day
- Magnesium at night and 3 × a day if the person is com-
ing off opioids
- Zinc 100mgs a day
- Saint Mary's Thistle daily (Silybum Marianum) liver
detoxification
- Borage oil EFAs, reduces inflammation and pain
- Lavender oil on the pillow and collar is an
anti-depressant
- B1 daily in the case of alcoholics
- B12 daily in the case of alcoholics

As a naturopath, I practise biofunctional naturopathic medicine
and I can also ask for a series of tests depending on the client's
presentation, so the blood assay I order levels for includes:
- Fasting glucose (alcohol is a lipid; it dysregulates glucose
metabolism)
- Triglycerides, cholesterol (can be high in alcoholics and
addicts eating a poor diet)
- B1 (alcoholics can be depleted)
- B12 (addicts generally have poor diets which can lead to
low levels)
- Vitamin D (addicts generally have poor diets and are
often photophobic which can lead to low levels)
- HIV, hep B and C (needle contamination and poor
sexual practices)
- Liver and kidney function tests (damage is present in
many addicts)

- Cortisol (addicts often have an adrenal gland dysfunction)
- TSH, T3r, T3, T4 (TSH alone may not show thyroid dysregulation)
- DHEA (addicts may have low levels)
- Red and white blood cell count (indicators of oxidative stress and infection)
- Full mineral count (mineral imbalances can lead to behavioural problems)
- MTHFR gene test (positive results can produce behavioural issues due to problems with the folate cycle)
- Hair mineral analysis (looking for heavy metals and mineral dysregulation)

Added to this homework are some cognitive/behavioural awareness questionnaires and instructions that the client must complete between sessions. They are exercises in living mindfully.

Naturopathically my job is not just to help the patient stop using the substance but also to guide them to health. In allopathic medicine, the absence of obvious infection, malformation, trauma and mental instability is considered health. Clement (2007) instructs us that in naturopathic medicine health is considered the presence of vitality of body and mind in harmony with nature: 'vis medicatrix naturae' (the healing power of nature).

Donovan (1995) reported that between one-third and one-half of patients fail to comply to the clinician's advice and instructions which results in major treatment failures. Each client comes to us with different abilities. Some will task well and complete their homework and some will struggle for a variety of reasons. Patient compliance is something we aim towards as clinicians and therapists and even more as hypnotists, but life is never simple.

Treatment should never be rigid and must always adapt to the individual client's specific needs. While I teach you the six steps a client needs to go through to become clean and sober, sometimes issues come up in therapy and we have to use the step that will address those issues at that time. The inflexible therapist is but a mere parrot copying chapter and verse verbatim from others and ignoring the needs of the client as an individual.

Barkan (2017) observes that higher socioeconomic groups tend to experience better health outcomes because they are exposed to less stress and poverty and have more resources. Patients with education, time, favourable social circumstances and money can complete homework more easily because it is within their abilities. In some cases, however, this is not true, as some such clients can deprioritise therapy, lowering its value to that of shopping or a hairdressing appointment. In such cases I am inclined to explain the gravitas of their situation and refer to the contractual obligation they gave by entering into the therapeutic agreement, and explain that my time is reserved for those who are seriously committed to achieving sobriety.

Jin, Sklar, Min Sen Oh, & Chuen (2008), in reviewing 101 studies, discovered that many found that lower socioeconomic groups experience poorer health outcomes due to lack of resources, support, education and money. The review also found that short-term therapy produced higher compliance. For some of these clients I may reduce the homework list to the bare essentials so they are able to manage success, therefore increasing their belief in their abilities, and achieve what might be absolutely necessary. There are, however, those in this group who excel at complying to requests as they value the ability to have therapy very highly. When sometimes they achieve their goals against what seems all the odds, I am humbled by their efforts and achievements.

Unless you are a social worker or carrying out an emergency assessment/counselling situation, I advise you to keep therapy in the therapy room, even the same room if possible. The expectations of both hypnosis and therapeutic change are locational and situationally bound. The client enters into the trance of being assisted by the hypnotherapist to change and change fast. All the associations for new trance states and therapeutic change come back into play automatically when the client enters into subsequent sessions, and you trigger continuation of therapy. Even when I see someone 20 years later, they go into a trance as soon as they are in the therapy chair opposite my desk. Twelve thousand miles away from where I started practising, the same therapy chair sits opposite the same desk I took halfway around the world.

There are no clients I like or clients I dislike, as everyone who comes through the clinic door has hired me to deliver the best result I can for them. My job is to give them everything I can for their money and often more when they need it. If I am asking the client to change and do something different, I must demonstrate my flexibility and commitment to helping them achieve their goals.

Another principle of naturopathic medicine is the therapist as teacher, so you must teach, not just preach. Clients read you as a therapist, and even as a hypnotist, so if you play the game of top dog and bottom dog, it breaks rapport with the client. When you genuinely display that you are on your client's side and giving them everything you have, it increases the therapeutic alliance and lowers resistance.

I instruct my clients, "Get the most you can out of therapy and make sure you get your money's worth", and of course this is said with humour. Sigmund Freud (1990) wrote a book on humour in therapy and how that was an essential part of communication that provoked the intellect. Furman & Ahola (1988) talked about using humorous anecdotes and jokes in therapy to help the client deframe, reframe and gain alternative perspectives on their world view.

At the end of the session when the client has learnt Steps 1, 2 and 3 of the program, they leave with their homework, which they will do constantly over the next two weeks, and I ask: "Did you have a good time?"

Then:

"Did you achieve what you came to achieve today?"

I saw Simon every four weeks and he made a full recovery over six months. He saw the family doctor I recommended who, on my request and in agreement with it, withdrew each medication at a time. His previous family doctor had incompetently turned Simon into a drug addict, not recognising that he was in circumstantial trauma. His parents watched him to see if he had any problems, but in fact his recovery was expedient and the lack of medications gave him back his ability to think and use his mind. His old family doctor telephoned me and was angry that I had referred him elsewhere and I simply explained he was now under a new family physician.

Part of the work I did with Simon was to rebuild his confidence so he could go back out into the world and resume his identity as a proud, functioning man. After the fourth month his wife contacted him to meet up as she had left the man she ran off with, but Simon refused contact with her and filed for divorce. On the seventh month he started a new sales job and got on with his life.

American Psychiatric Association. (2013). *Diagnostic and statistical manual of mental disorders* (5th ed.). Arlington, VA: Author.

Barkan, S. E. (2017). *Health, illness, and society: An introduction to medical sociology.* Lanham, MD: Rowman & Littlefield.

Berman, S., O'Neill, J., Fears, S., Bartzokis, G., & London, E. D. (2008). Abuse of amphetamines and structural abnormalities in the brain. *Annals of the New York Academy of Sciences, 1141,* 195–220. doi:10.1196/annals.1441.031

Brown, P. (1994). Toward a psychobiological model of dissociation and post-traumatic stress disorder. In S.J. Lynn et al. (Ed.), *Dissociation: Clinical and theoretical perspectives.* New York, NY: Guilford.

Clement, B. (2007). *Hippocrates: Lifeforce.* Summertown, TN: Healthy Living.

Donovan, J. L. (1995). Patient decision making: The missing ingredient in compliance research. *International Journal of Technology Assessment in Health Care, 11*(3), 443–455. doi:10.1017/S0266462300008667

First, M. B., Reed, G. M., Hyman, S. E., & Saxena, S. (2015). The development of the ICD –11 clinical descriptions and diagnostic guidelines for mental and behavioural disorders. *World Psychiatry, 14*(1), 82–90. doi:10.1002/wps.20189

Freud, S. (1990). *Jokes and their relation to the unconscious* (J. Strachey, Trans.). New York, NY: W. W. Norton.

Furman, B., & Ahola, T. (1988). The use of humour in brief therapy. *Journal of Strategic and Systemic Therapies, 7*(2), 3–20. doi:10.1521/jsst.1988.7.2.3

Griffith, J. L., & Griffith, M. E. (1994). *The body speaks: Therapeutic dialogues for mind-body problems.* New York, NY: Basic Books.

Hilgard, E. R., & Hilgard, J. R. (1994). *Hypnosis in the relief of pain* (Rev ed.). Abingdon, United Kingdom: Routledge.

Hull, C. L. (2002). *Hypnosis and suggestibility.* Bancyfelin, Wales: Crown House.

Jin, J., Sklar, G. E., Min Sen Oh, V., & Chuen Li, S. (2008). Factors affecting therapeutic compliance: A review from the patient's perspective. *Therapeutics and Clinical Risk Management, 4*(1), 269–286.

Lambert, S. (1996). The effects of hypnosis/guided imagery on the postoperative course of children. *Journal of Developmental and Behavioral Pediatrics, 17*(5), 307–310.

Lovern, J. D. (1991) *Pathways to reality: Erickson-inspired approaches to chemical dependency.* New York, NY: Brunner-Routledge.

Rosen, S. (1991). *My voice will go with you: The teaching tales of Milton H. Erickson.* New York, NY: W. W. Norton.

Rothschild, B. (2000). *The body remembers: The psychophysiology of trauma and trauma treatment.* New York, NY: W. W. Norton.

Santen, F. J., Sofsky, J., Bilic, N., & Lippert, R. (1975). Mechanism of action of narcotics in the production of menstrual dysfunction in women. *Fertility and Sterility, 26*(6), 538–548.

Segerstrom, S. C., & Miller, G. E. (2004). Psychological stress and the human immune system: A meta-analytic study of 30 years of inquiry. *Psychological Bulletin, 130*(4), 601–630. doi:10.1037/0033-2909.130.4.601

Torvik, A., Lindboe, C. F., & Rogde, S. (1982). Brain lesions in alcoholics: A neuropathological study with clinical correlations. *Journal of the Neurological Sciences, 56*(2–3), 233–248.

Wolinsky, P., & Ryan, M. O. (1991). *Trances people live.* Wilton Manors, FL: Bramble Books.

Yapko, M. D. (2001). *Treating depression with hypnosis: Integrating cognitive-behavioral and strategic approaches.* Abingdon, United Kingdom: Routledge.

How Did You Get There?

The interminable question of how addicts become addicted has a variety of proposed explanations. Some of the original medical explanations of addiction were based on an old experiment that gave isolated rats in cages the choice between pure water and opioid-laced water. The hypothesis was that once exposed to the drug-laced water, the rat would be physically addicted to the substance and their addiction was physical.

Rat Park was another experiment carried out in the late 1970s and published in 1981 (Alexander, Beyerstein, Hadaway, & Coambs, 1981). It involved placing 16–20 mixed-sex rats in a so-called stimulating environment in which there were many toys for them to play with and other rats to keep them company and occupied. They had the choice of water dispensers, with one containing pure tap water and the other opioid-laced water. The hypothesis was that because they were socialised they would choose to drink less water from the opioid-laced dispenser and that is what was reported. Alexander et al. proposed that drugs do not cause addiction, but environment does.

Both of these theories lack rigour and testability (as well as being ethically unsound). Human beings are not rats. Rats are not exposed to advertising, religious views, peer pressure to take drugs, entertainment that glamorises addiction, human social attitudes, the pressure of having to work a 60-hour week, and a host of other variables that affect humans and not rats. Neither were those rats exposed to a number of different potentially addictive substances with different effects. If the researchers' hypothesis was proved, then why do wealthy, privileged people like Frederick Hervey, the eighth Marquess of Bristol, Princess Margaret and the Duchess of York become dependent on a variety of substances, when they enjoy the freedom of being able to live their lives as they wish?

Tracie: *So it's been three weeks since I saw you Jenny. We did the first three steps of the program last time and you went away and followed my instructions. How have you changed?*

Jenny: *I don't know where to begin really. I haven't been out to a club. Not taken any Es, [MDMA], coke or even smoked a joint or had a drink. I never stop getting texts from people asking where I am, what's happened to me and asking when I'm coming out.*

Tracie: *So you've been clean and sober?*

Jenny: *Yep I've done nothing. Actually I mean I've taken nothing but I've done everything I'd stopped doing over the past six months like eating, taking care of myself, going to the gym, focusing on my work. It's a bit freaky really because some days I get up, look in the mirror and think: 'Who are you?'*

Tracie: *Is that good?*

Jenny: *Yep it's brilliant. I didn't realise how skinny and sick I was looking until I've actually stopped putting drugs up my nose or down my throat or drawing on a joint. The first few days I was really sick and on a really bad comedown but it passed and I got myself together.*

Tracie: *You can be really proud of yourself.*

Jenny: *I don't know about proud. I'm more shocked that I could do it because my brain was pretty fried. I'd gotten so deep into the drug scene where people are dropping stuff almost daily. I'd forgotten what it must be like to be straight and normal. I thought normal was boring and only people who didn't know better weren't taking drugs. Last weekend I went to my parents' house and saw my two daughters for the first time in six weeks.*

Tracie: *That was a really big thing to do; well done.*

Jenny: *Oh my God, I just lied to you. I can't believe I just did that. I did go out one night after I saw my daughters. It was just the one and I was going out four and five nights a week before and taking drugs for seven years. I took some coke that night. Two days later I got back on the program. I feel so stupid for lying to you and taking it. I really regret it as I was doing so well.*

Tracie: *So 20 days out of 21 you were clean and sober. And you remained on the program for 18 days. You're definitely going in the right direction. You can remember the last time I saw you, you learnt steps 1, 2 and 3 of the 6 Step Recovery Program. Step 1 is Staying Out of Denial. Where were you when you relapsed?*

Jenny: *In denial.*

Tracie: *How did that work for you?*

Jenny: *It didn't.*

Tracie: *Will you make that mistake again?*

Jenny: *No.*

Relapse recovery intentions

1. Relapses happen with some clients for many reasons and therapists need to allow clients to talk about that without them feeling like failures, guilty, shameful or having betrayed the therapy.
2. As you deal with those issues, trigger the safety anchor.
3. You must acknowledge the relapse, deal with the issue and the client's distress around the relapse, but do not focus therapy on the relapse; focus it on recovery.
4. Reframe the situation by looking for times when the client has succeeded in being clean and sober and focus the client's mind on those times to strengthen their sense of self-efficacy.

Relapse recovery trance script

(Tracie): Close your eyes Jenny and make yourself comfortable… (re-induction)…you know you were not born an addict (truism, fact recall)…there is no evidence of genetic transmission of addictive behaviours (truism, fact)…**interesting with your eyes closed now seeing the many times you are clean and sober** (grammatical incongruency causing confusion, transderivational search, fact recall, indirect suggestion)…you can remember those each one remember time those (word salad, confusion, transderivational search, recall)…when you were a child (regression, recall)… times as a teenager and times you don't use that substance (regression, recall for sobriety ability)…**up inside your head how do you look clean and sober** (recall, regression, time shift to present, indirect suggestion)…you have those memories that go with you wherever you go (regression, identification of abilities, future pacing)…you can recall those memories wherever you go (repetition, post-hypnotic suggestion)…**in an instant you can see yourself clean and sober now** (intra-hypnotic suggestion, post-hypnotic suggestion)…I want you to know you were not born an addict (repetition, truism, fact, dissolving old beliefs)…there is no evidence of genetic transmission of addictive behaviours (truism, indirect suggestion) **you can know you want a clean and sober path** (intra-hypnotic suggestion, post-hypnotic suggestion)... being clean and sober is a major cornerstone of your life (suggestion for shift in values and criteria of needs)...every breath... every hour...every hour of the rest of your life (contingent suggestion, general time frame suggestions)...it is so clear in your mind that (preparation for suggestion, ego-strengthening)...**you are clean and sober** (intra-hypnotic suggestion)...one of the major tenets of your life (appealing to the super-ego)...every time you fall down you get back up and start again (suggestion for Schopenhauer's 'Will to life', survival instinct)...and again...**and again as you break that old addictive habit** (fractionation, suggestion for behavioural change)...falling in love with yourself as a (association to self, ego-strengthening, reassociating to self-agency).... **clean and sober Jenny more and more and more every day** (direct suggestion, post-hypnotic suggestion, fractionation)... opening your eyes and smiling at me (somnambulism).

I do not subscribe to any singular theory of addiction. During my clinical practice I have observed that people become substance-dependent for five basic reasons, which can at times be multiple. The drivers of addictions are:

1. *Modelling* – copying what other people are doing, even inter-generationally and inter-culturally.
2. *Peer pressure* – acquiescing to what others think we should be doing, which includes health professionals, friends, families and the law, or developing a sense we should be doing what others are doing.
3. *Thrill-seeking/exploration* – exploring the mind through substances and seeking high levels of adventure without risk assessment.
4. *Social defiance* – an anti-establishment frame of mind

where the person engages in activities simply because it is considered anti-social.

5. *Withdrawing from the world* – a defensive mechanism where people find interacting with the world too stressful and hard, so they dissociate by any means.

Every addict of any kind can fit into one or more of these categories, and by addicts I am also including people who do not consider themselves addicts and are over-users of the substance of choice. In this I am including people who have become addicted to prescription medications due to advice or pressure to use those medications.

The psychiatrist Wolberg (1945) wrote about how, when using hypnosis with hypnoanalytical techniques, the client is able to retrieve memories more quickly than psychoanalytical techniques. He explained that not every patient has the luxury of being able to spend extended time and money in therapy and a more abbreviated form of therapy was needed. Every addict holds in their memories the keys to the drivers of their addiction.

There has, however, unfortunately been much paranoia around hypnotic regression in recent years due to some high-profile legal cases, mainly in the US, where therapists were sued for inducing False Memory Syndrome around sexual abuse. Freud is blamed for this as he backed away from hypnosis and hypnotic regression when he discovered many of his female patients had been sexually abused and their relatives threatened to sue him (Mollon, 2000). Instead, to protect himself legally and stop himself being sued by relatives, he declared those memories to be fantasy or hysteria.

Barba (1995), in Campbell's edited collection of papers and essays on broken memories, suggests that many of our memories may be false and confabulations. We constantly alter our memories to facilitate the needs, circumstances and demands of today. This is particularly borne out when we look at evidence witnesses

189

give in court cases where the more witnesses the court calls to testify, the more versions of an incident are presented, until the real facts are indiscernible. Kuhns (1981) tells us this is one of the reasons why hypnotically retrieved memories are not generally allowed to be used as reliable memory retrieval in court cases.

Morrison (2001) tells us that in the hands of the consummate, well-trained professional, the discovery of psychodynamic drivers and conflicts during analytical hypnotherapy can indeed help the client understand the problems they were experiencing. It also helps the therapist to be able to guide them in a more resourceful direction when the therapist discovers their behavioural drivers.

From a therapeutic amelioration perspective, however, memories do not necessarily need to be true but only useful in moving the client forward. As hypnotherapists we are constantly inducing supplementary memories. Erickson (2009) in *The February Man* described how he repeatedly placed himself in the client's memories during trance as a reassuring adult because the client had a very unhappy childhood which was disturbing him.

As hypnotherapists we are constantly creating amnesia and supplementing memories. In the case of recovery from addiction, the client must have some idea of what behaviours they need to do or avoid in their future so they do not resume the addictive behaviour. They may not retrieve 'the truth, the whole truth and nothing but the truth', but we work with what they retrieve.

Tracie: *Today we are going to focus on Steps 4, 5 and 6. You know it can be useful to know why you became so involved in taking drugs and ending up as a multiple drug-using addict. And we have established you are an addict. Even though you have managed to hang on to your job in the advertising agency, you lost custody of your children to your parents last year. Do you agree you're an addict?*

Jenny: Yes.

Tracie: So how much drugs or alcohol can you take in the future?

Jenny: None.

Tracie: Step 4 is called. 'How Did You Get There?' It's about you learning how and why you became an addict in the first place. It's very useful for you to know what drove your behaviours in the past, so that you do not repeat them and can avoid doing the addiction again. Does that make sense?

Jenny: Yes.

Tracie: It's really not rocket science, just plain common sense. You know, I had a client recently who discovered she was taking drugs and drinking because she knew it annoyed her husband. The marriage was not working and she wanted out, so she would get drunk and take drugs three or four times a week to annoy him, hoping he would leave her. We all do things for a reason, but sometimes we do things without yet knowing the reasons we are acting that way. There are some therapies just based on people knowing why they do things and in the 6 Step Program we have this stage where you can become aware of what your drivers were behind your addiction, so you can devise different behaviours in future.

Step 4 – How Did You Get There? intentions

1. All learned and adaptive behaviours are either installed or adaptions to circumstances. There is no evidence that addiction is genetic. Therefore, all addictive behaviours have

roots, causes and drivers.

2. Cognitive awareness of how a person makes mistakes can help them to avoid those mistakes in the future.
3. Most addicts have forgotten consciously how they got into problems with addictive substances in the first place.
4. Regression in hypnosis helps the client know where they were when they had problems in the past and become aware of what they need to do to avoid addictive behaviours in the future.

Step 4 – How Did You Get There? trance script
(Tracie): OK Jenny close your eyes and be comfortable (state shift to deeper trance)…one of the most important parts of recovery from addiction is to know how you got there in the first place (suggestion for self-awareness)…let your eyes remain closed as you relax more (fractionation)…**you can be safe once again in my office** (triggering the safety anchor)…as your body sits there safe your mind can go back in time to the very first time you took that substance (regression)…you can be there in yourself (time orientation to past)…**tell me where you are** (transderivational search, interrogative suggestion for regression – wait for the answer)…**tell me how old are you** (interrogative deepener – wait for the answer)…**tell me who are you with** (interrogative deepener for full trance – wait for the answer)…you know there is always a reason someone starts to take a substance (generalised suggestion for emerging memory)…**tell me do you have the substance or do they** (wait for the answer)…take yourself to two seconds just before you first took that substance (suggestion for pre-addiction awareness)…just examine your mind now (time orientation for regression)…**tell me what do you hope to get from the experience** (pacing in regression, suggestion for cognitive awareness, wait for the answer) and it is interesting to think about that isn't it (transderivational search, interrogative suggestion to maintain regression)…I would like you to come all the way through time back up to today and back all

the way through time back to when you first took that substance (time scanning)…examine every single time you took that substance (transderivational search, direct suggestion for self-analysis)…**tell me knowing what you know now** (suggestion for comparison)…**was it worth it** (transderivational search, double bind for discounting the value of those drug-taking experiences – wait for answer)…**you will remember that always wherever you are** (post-hypnotic suggestion for retaining the discounting of those memories, negative hallucination in that it omits positive memories of drug taking)…**awake…asleep wherever you are** (fractionation to overcome resistance)…**you will remember taking that substance does not work for you** (suggestion for seeding the idea that taking that substance does not give positive results in all time frames)…you can bring back your awareness that taking (awareness recall)…**that substance does not work for you** (intra-hypnotic suggestion, post-hypnotic suggestion)… opening your eyes and smiling at me (good internal kinaesthetic feeling associated with not taking the substance, somnambulism)…**and clean and sober does work for you doesn't it** (interrogative suggestion, somnambulism, yes set with head nod prompt)…yes that's really true isn't it (head nod prompt, yes set)…and you don't want to change your mind do you (head shake prompt, establishing ratification, lock the gate)…you never want to take that substance again do you (head shake prompt, verifying ratification)…**falling in love with yourself as clean and sober** (ego-strengthening, positive internal kinaesthetic).

Jenny: *I didn't realise that.*

Tracie: *Hi – you didn't realise what … that you now realise?*

Jenny: *I was a latchkey kid. I did know but I didn't realise how it affected me?*

Tracie:	How did that affect you?
Jenny:	My parents came from Greece to live in Australia. I was the only child and they worked in the restaurant all the time to make a good life for us.
Tracie:	What did that mean for you?
Jenny:	I was alone. There was no one at home when I came home from school. I was lonely. I didn't feel loved. Didn't feel important.
Tracie:	How did that lead to addiction?
Jenny:	When I started to sneak off to bars and clubs when I was 14 and 15 and take drugs, I felt confident and felt like I was really important. I became the party girl and I thought people loved me.
Tracie:	Were you confident?
Jenny:	I think I thought taking drugs, hanging out in clubs and parties became my life. I was noisy and everyone wanted me at their party because I was the party girl. I thought I was confident.
Tracie:	Did you feel confident when you lost custody of your children to your parents?
Jenny:	No. It all started to go to shit when I got pregnant. I knew I shouldn't take drugs but I couldn't help myself. Then when I got pregnant the second time, my parents knew I was taking drugs. After the second child they petitioned for custody, citing me as an unfit mother and won. The fathers were on the drug scene themselves and not interested. It was horrible.

Rogers & Frason (2015) stated one of the most important parts of all therapy is active listening. A client may never have vocalised their internal world before, for fear of being judged, simply did not have access to anyone with whom they could talk, or could not find the language. When giving permission to vocalise, the client feels acknowledged and that someone is paying attention to them and listening to their issues.

Bandler & MacDonald (1989) suggest that vocalising is changing the internal kinaesthetic feelings into an auditory expression and changing the modality of operation, which can give a different perspective on an experience to help break behavioural patterns. Not only is this a process of changing modalities of experience, but also exposing subtle sub-modality issues that might not be working for the client that the therapist has not noticed before. It can, at times, cause an automatic reframe for the client, but also give more clues to the therapist what might be happening with the client so the therapist can provoke further change.

Andreas & Andreas (1994) show how people are often seeking and pursuing fundamental deep, core, human experiences such as love, peace and acceptance. These basic human drivers can frequently be pursued in unhealthy ways because the client is unresourceful and unable to find a way to pursue them in wholesome, rewarding ways. Those drivers will never cease seeking these basic fundamental human needs, as the needs come from the id; therapy, however, can help the client find better ways to fulfil those needs.

Jenny: *No, losing my children to the custody of my parents was totally humiliating and it hurt me. I know I was doing too many drugs and it was probably the right thing to happen, but it still hurt me deeply, so I just took more drugs to push that hurt down.*

Tracie: *So let me ask you some questions Jenny. You say you got involved in clubs, parties and drugs to*

feel good. Does that feel good if you do
that today?

Jenny: Oh my God, no. I'm beginning to see I really fucked
up.

Tracie: So how much drugs or alcohol is right for you in
your life now?

Jenny: None ever because I need to focus on my children and try and put things right.

Tracie: You say you thought that partying and doing
drugs or alcohol with other people helped you
feel important and loved. If you did those substances with those people or any other people in
the future, would they be loving you?

Jenny: No. And I don't want my children to grow up
lonely and feeling abandoned like I did.

Tracie: So what do you want for them?

Jenny: I want them to grow up knowing I love them.

Tracie: In the future can you do that taking drugs or
alcohol?

Jenny: Hell no.

Tracie: And what do you want for you?

Jenny: I want love in my life. I want them to love me
and I want them to know I love them.

Tracie: Are you ready to stop being that desperate
14-year-old, mature into an adult, be clean and
sober and focus on your children? Because that's
what it takes. I'm sure your parents loved you in
their own way and thought running the restau-
rant was a way to make money to secure your

*future. Maybe they didn't understand how lonely
you were and perhaps thought they had been
giving you love?*

Jenny: *That's a lot.*

Tracie: *You're right. Being an adult does take a lot. It comes
with the territory. It comes with taking on the responsibility of being a parent. You just take it one
step at a time like the rest of us, who are doing
adult. I can't promise you that every day will be
easy; in fact, some days will be really hard, but
you do it anyway because that's what you do as
an adult. That's what a parent does.*

Jenny: *OK, I'll try.*

Tracie: *No such thing as try. Do or don't do, (Yoda).*

Jenny: *Jesus, Tracie, you're tough.*

Tracie: *That's what you pay me for. That's what you
are. Tougher than addiction, tougher than your
drug-taking friends. Tough enough to be clean
and sober. Tough enough to really love and allow
yourself to be loved by your family. Drugs and
alcohol will never give you love. Tough enough
to work that love for yourself and your children
every single day by being clean and sober. Love is
what you do…not just what you say.*

People are frequently racked with guilt and shame about the
things they have done and the way they have lived their lives
when they were addicts. They know they did not have control but
society programs people to feel shame and guilt around addiction as it is frequently seen as a moral fault. Gold (2012) wrote
about how governments considered removing financial state

benefits from addicts who would not attend therapy, thereby creating a class of addicts who could only turn to crime to fund their addictions.

According to the moral model operated in fundamental Christian religious movements in the US, addiction is a failure in a person's moral code. Mason (2016) states the person has entered into the realms of sin and immorality and has chosen how they go forward and make choices. An addict is seen as a person who has moved away from God's teachings. Islam teaches moderation in all things and says, "O Children of Adam! Wear your beautiful apparel at every time and place of prayer: Eat and drink: But waste not by excess, for Allah loveth not the wasters." [Al-Quran 7:31] (Ali, 2002).

For addicts, addiction is a lack of resources. They are stranded in dependency without a map to escape the addiction. The job of the therapist is to guide the willing traveller on their journey and not to attribute shame or guilt regarding their action of addiction. Indeed, the addict needs to recover their self-esteem and strengthen their ego in order to control the greed of the id for the addictive substance. Guilt, shame or suggestion of moral depravity should never be used by the therapist to quell the addiction because it will damage the client's ego and ultimately be highly likely to lead to a relapse. It also damages the client's sense of self-agency, since they are seeing themselves being judged by a higher power.

The question of whether the therapist moving the client towards resolution should use the word 'addict' is a valid one. 'Addict' is a nominalisation of the action to be addicted. While 'addict' is not a verb, it can be used with a verb like 'to be' so it can be conjugated in the past, present and future tense. Szasz (2007), the psychiatrist, warned about how in medicine, psychiatry, mental health and therapy, giving patients labels can be seen as cementing them into acting out that identity, as with schizophrenia, depression or psychopathy. To some extent over-diagnosing is prevalent and driven by the pharmaceutical industries.

There is also the issue of patient self-inflicted guilt that comes with such labels. I do, however, believe that in the case of addiction where the client presents with a medical emergency, using the label 'addict' gives the client a firm foothold from where to recover. It is unquestionably nominal language that presents the client with a polar option of being an addict or not. In recovery from addiction, there is no grey area where a person can be half, a quarter or an eighth of an addict. Because addiction for most people is perceived as being beyond free will, I emphasise to clients that they will always be an addict but can be one who has recovered from addiction and can remain clean and sober.

Jenny: *Can my family ever forgive me for the way I behaved?*

Tracie: *They are your family. You might not have approved of the way your parents raised you but they love you enough to raise your daughters too and give you access to them. To your daughters you are just their mum and they are happy to see you. The real question is: Can you forgive yourself because if you want anyone to forgive you, just maybe you need to forgive yourself first. Perhaps you can allow yourself to heal.*

Healing the past intentions

1. Addicts can be racked with guilt by things they have done to maintain their addictions in the past.
2. Creating a healing experience for the client can help them move forward in their lives. Since this goes beyond the conscious hypercritical state to a deep hypnotic state, it can help with parts resolution, where one part of the mind comes to agreement with other parts.

3. The client needs to feel that they are important and cared for, since they have had times as an addict when they have seen themselves as an outcast.
4. We also know from research that taking people into states of hypnosis promotes repair of body systems, including the brain and restoring homeostasis.

Healing the past trance script

(Tracie): Jenny close your eyes and focus on you (focusing on herself)…as you have spent this time I wonder how you have put those ghosts to rest (conflict resolution)…perhaps you can let go of what has haunted you and what drove you to addiction (time orientation to present, demarcation between addiction and sobriety)…**allowing yourself to move forward as a clean and sober person** (future pacing sobriety)…your life has changed forever (ratification of unconscious change)…of course that is completely your choice and you can think about what you are choosing now (transderivational search, dissolving resistance, cognitive analysis, promoting self-agency)…**a forever life changed** (word salad, confusion, suggestion for change, ratification of change)…**the lives of those around you changed by the nature of you having changed** (ego-strengthening for self-agency and social awareness, future pacing)…you chose a one way ticket to a better future (ratification of change)…you can forgive yourself for the ravages of the past addiction (suggestion for release from guilt)…and you move on (future pacing)…move forward (future pacing)…leave the past behind and live in today (time orientation to the present)…**you can heal yourself** (suggestion for cognitive resolution)…you can grow (dissociation from the past)…you can be more than you were (dissociation from the past, ego-strengthening)…you can take up your place in the world (suggestion for self-agency, self-efficacy, repairing the ego)…**let a great light come over you** (positive hallucination)…surround you…within you…a healing light (conflict resolution)…let it permeate the whole of your being…let your scars soften (suggestion for self-care)…forgive yourself for your mistakes…be kind to the new you (future pace)…**heal now deeply and peacefully**…**deeply and peacefully now** (separation of past, present and future)…I want you to bring that sense of healing back with you to life (maintenance of separation of past, present and future)…feeling a deep sense of relief, strength, happiness now and in the future (intra-hypnotic, post-hypnotic suggestion)…**isn't it good to be the healthy happy you** (interrogative suggestion).

In considering why people who can recover from addiction became addicts, we must also look at those who do not recover or are not ready to recover. With clients I get a 90% recovery rate in private practice because I am careful in screening clients to see if they are ready to recover. Since I am in private practice, I have the luxury of being discerning about the clients I take on. When working in the public sector, hospital or charities you, as a therapist, may not have that option. The 10% who do not recover remain addicts for many reasons which I will discuss below.

In spending time speaking with a member of staff at my local Prince of Wales Hospital acute psychiatric ward in Sydney, which deals with emergency admissions, I am told many of their patients are revolving-door addicts. Most of them suffer from co-morbidity – that is to say, they already have some kind of mental illness, which is, unfortunately, exacerbated by drug and alcohol use and abuse.

Patients are usually scheduled from the community, then to emergency and then have to become involuntary patients in acute closed psychiatric wards. The staff member said high THC (cannabis), alcohol and ice are the most difficult addictions, as patients generally relapse as soon as they are discharged, become unwell again, and stop taking their medications.

In private practice I rarely see schizophrenic patients with addiction problems. The low level of social function that occurs with people experiencing schizophrenia and addiction leads most of them to be dependent on the welfare state, with lower socioeconomic circumstances, so they do not tend to access private medicine. While I occasionally see medicated schizophrenics for problems such as depression, lack of confidence or relationship problems, who can do well in therapy, I do not generally see them for addiction.

There are some groups that do come into private practice for help with addiction who do not do well.

The first are people experiencing borderline personality disorder (BPD). Their problems include being driven by insecurity, mistrust, rage, fear, attachment disorders and paranoia. Such personalities find it difficult to tolerate therapy. Difficulty arises for them because their world view is static and while they may initially be enthusiastic and engage in therapy, they can flip to another alter-personality that defends their static view of the world in an instant. The therapist helping them suddenly becomes the enemy, is to blame for all their problems and the client withdraws from therapy. People experiencing BPD may have experienced early life trauma and have a desperate need to continually identify as a victim.

The second group are people experiencing self-sabotage personality disorder. While this group of patients may bond with a therapist, they will sabotage any results they have achieved. This has become such an ingrained behaviour that they are not generally consciously aware they are doing it but sometimes they can be aware. They have a damaged belief system, low self-esteem and will seek the benefits of being an addict, even though they have said they want to stop the addiction. The secondary gains they get from being an addict often outweigh the benefits of staying in treatment and trying to become clean and sober.

Thirdly there are those clients who are not committed to therapy. I provide intense, fast-paced therapy that requires full engagement from the client and I hold clients accountable for their participation. People come into therapy for many reasons, including guilt about their addiction, because of pressure from relatives, friends, people at work or the courts, but this group is not truly committed to therapy, so do not do well.

In the private sector, I also see sociopaths and psychopaths coming into the clinic for addiction cessation. Both are often able to hold down a job and make money so are able to access services in the private sector. Therapists often think these personality types have difficulty managing in society but that is only partly true as they can become quite successful.

Sociopaths live in a world where they are engaging with constant confabulation, even before the complications of addiction are added. They find it impossible to constantly operate reality-testing and are compulsive liars and deceivers. This offers challenges during treatment as they are unable to fully understand Step 1: Staying Out of Denial. Not only do they constantly lie to others but also to themselves, and this includes issues around their addictions. Efforts to help them stock their superego with useful values and safe codes of living often produce only temporary changes in their behaviours.

Psychopaths find it difficult to take direction from others. When faced with direct suggestion and commands, they can become defensive, dismissive and aggressive, finding therapy too hard to tolerate. Their need to dominate and conquer frequently overrides their need to stay safe and be well. When challenged, a psychopath may leave therapy without ever contacting the therapist again, or complain the therapist did not do their job because they did not magically stop the client's addiction.

I have found for addiction cessation success it is likely that both sociopaths and psychopaths will need to be in long-term psychotherapy. While these two personality types may be able to enter hypnosis successfully, they generally do not do well with hypnotherapy as they are unable to follow post-hypnotic suggestions or treatment protocols.

There are wildly estimated studies that show anything from

about 5% to 40% of the general population may have mental health issues. These studies are impossible to interpret and generalise because the classification of mental health disorders varies from country to country and culture to culture. Such data is driven by variables including language, cultural perspectives, differing medical health systems, legal issues and government financial strategies.

Also, research bias is always strong. For the population experiencing addiction and further mental health issues, we can be sure the incidence of co-pathology is far higher. The frequency with which you will encounter those clients with additional mental health issues will depend on what client population you are servicing. If a client experiences co-pathologies, those must also be treated in order to establish addiction recovery as a stable, clean and sober way of living. If you are not qualified to treat those disorders, you need to refer the client on.

I saw Jenny for a further five months and she did not use drugs or alcohol again. After three months clean and sober she moved into her parents' annex cottage at the bottom of their garden and her parents and children lived in the main house. At work she changed to working part-time as she had no accommodation bills to pay and this allowed her to spend more time with her daughters. She gave up partying and going to nightclubs or hanging out with her old drug-using friends with the aim of one day getting custody of her daughters. Her life changed completely and, as she said, she was beginning to try to get things right in the future and gain people's trust. She knew that would take a long time but became determined to do what she had to do to make it happen.

Chapter 8 References

Alexander, B. K., Beyerstein, B. L., Hadaway, P. F., & Coambs, R.B. (1981). Effect of early and later colony housing on oral ingestion of morphine in rats. *Pharmacology Biochemistry and Behavior, 15*(4), 571–576.

Ali, M. M. (2002). *The holy Qur'an with English translation and commentary* (7th ed.). Dublin, OH: Ahamadiyya Anjuman Isha'at-Islam.

Andreas, C., & Andreas, T. (1994). *Core transformation: Reaching the wellspring within.* Boulder, CO: Real People Press.

Barba, G. D. (1995). Consciousness and confabulation: Remembering "another" past. In R. Campbell & M. Conway (Eds.), *Broken memories: Case studies in memory impairment* (pp. 101–114). Oxford, United Kingdom: Blackwell.

Bandler, R., & MacDonald, W. (1989). *An insider's guide to sub-modalities.* Capitola, CA: Meta.

Erickson, M. (2009). *The February man: Evolving consciousness and identity in hypnotherapy.* Abingdon, United Kingdom: Routledge.

Gold, T. (2012, May 29). Is addiction a moral defect or a mental illness? *The Guardian.* Retrieved from https://www.theguardian.com/

Kuhns, B. (1981). *Hypnosis and the law.* London, England: Westwood.

Mason, M. K. (2016). *Addiction and God: Reconciling science with the spirit.* Bloomington, IN: WestBowPress.

Mollon, P. (2000). *Freud and false memory syndrome.* Thriplow, United Kingdom: Totem Books.

Morrison, J. (2001). *Analytical hypnotherapy, volume 1: Theoretical principles.* Bancyfelin, Wales: Crown House.

Rogers, C. & Frason, R. E. (2015). *Active listening.* Eastford, CT: Martino.

Szasz, T. (2007). *The medicalization of everyday life.* Syracuse, NY: Syracuse University Press.

Wolberg, L. R. (1945). *Hypno-analysis.* New York, NY: Grune & Stratton.

9 *Boundaries*

The boundary between the use and abuse of drugs and alcohol is not defined by the addict. By the very nature of addiction, the addict did not know where the line between substance use and substance abuse lay. No one sets out to be a drug addict or alcoholic. While a person may intellectually comprehend the dangers of substance use or abuse, when they cross the line into abuse and addiction, they have lost all rationale around that intellectual knowledge. If the addict knew where that dangerous line lay before they developed addiction, they probably would not have become an addict. As the addict approaches the line between drug use and drug abuse, they develop a negative hallucination for that boundary.

As humans we have developed a large brain and become a highly organised species. DeCasien, Williams, & Higham (n.d.) have analysed that we evolved as a fruit-foraging-and-eating ape species which required us to be highly organised in knowing where to find our food. Fruit is a high nutrition food that may have been responsible for helping grow the brain. There is a possibility that we may even have become bipedal because we were always reaching up for food. This also required us to be able to distinguish very clearly between safe food and poisons as well as negotiate complex social structures and territories. So human beings are reliant on knowing their physical, mental and social boundaries.

Piaget (Campbell, 1976) discussed child development when the adolescent gains hypothetico-deductive methods that enable them to perform greater reasoning and more self-analytical skills. This evolution of individual deductive reasoning is influenced by many factors, including health, environment, parental influence, education, social norms, peer pressure, economic status and arrestation of development due to trauma. The addict is an under-developed, immature personality incapable of the ability to implement and maintain good boundaries in their life, so they are unable to distinguish safe substances from poisons. They may even have had those reasoning abilities prior to addiction but lost them as addiction took hold.

Tracie: *Steven Step 5 of recovery is maintaining good boundaries in your life. What do you think that means?*

Steven: *I'm not really sure.*

Tracie: *Good answer and an opportunity for you to learn good boundaries. You may remember as a child your mother using the word 'No', to keep you safe, when you put your hands towards the stove. Perhaps when you started to ride a bicycle you were asked to stay in the yard, the park or on the pavement as you learnt your riding skills. At school you learnt not to pick fights with the school boxing champion. Do you remember those things?*

Steven: *Yeah, that's been my problem Tracie. I did anything my mother asked me, and my family and particularly my brother who introduced me to meth three years ago. I'm a bit of a people pleaser. I don't like to let people down. I want to please everyone.*

Tracie: *Everyone?*

Steven: Yeah, pretty much everyone, even my mates. 'Easy Stevo' they called me at school.

Tracie: How did that work out for you?

Steven: I got involved with my brother's schemes of building houses and when the financial collapse happened in 2008 we couldn't sell them. I managed to keep my house but the company went bankrupt and I lost a load of money that me and my wife had worked for over the years. I felt really stupid, my wife was very angry with me and I became so depressed I couldn't work for about a year. I was on anti-depressants and the doctor tried to tell me I was bipolar. My wife got me off the anti-depressants but then I was smoking weed for quite a while.

Tracie: You said when we talked about Step 4 that your brother has a long history of drugs and with him being the older brother, you often used to follow what he did without really questioning his actions. I would be stupid to not see why you didn't learn about good boundaries to keep you safe and I'm sure you would not want to pay a stupid person.

Steven: Yeah, one of us has got to be smart.

Katherine (1994) writes about how people constantly get into trouble in their lives when they are unaware of their personal boundaries and are transgressing other people's boundaries. Most people are not even aware what boundaries are or that they need strong personal boundaries in their lives to keep them safe and well. When people constantly transgress boundaries, they find themselves in positions of failure, often without even understanding what happened to them and how it happened.

Hansen & Graham (1991) discussed the importance of peer pressure resistance training with adolescents, as opposed to just expecting social norms to protect young people against the journey towards addiction. This, however, is true for people who become addicts at any age. We have moved through an age of political correctness where therapists have been afraid to separate their addiction clients from the people who contribute towards their addiction, particularly when those influences include the clients' own relatives.

In helping people recover from addiction, it is paramount to help them establish clean and sober boundaries that protect them from regressing back into addictive behaviour. This is a reviewing and learning process for the client in an area of personal control that they may never have been aware of before. No amount of medications, psychiatric confinement or legal control can teach a person to become clean and sober because it is a behaviour they need to learn as they mature their personality.

Tracie: *You know I'm struck by how polite you are and how your face lights up when you talk about your wife and children with the look of love in your eyes. How you get up every morning at 5.00am all week long, go and work as a carpenter on the building site and then find time for your children at the weekends. How you have kept your family together all these years despite personal problems and your company going bankrupt. And now you're running a crew of four other carpenters, plus yourself. It seems to me you are smart. It seems to me that in many areas of your life you are operating good boundaries. I wonder if you could take those skills you use to create good boundaries in your work and apply those to being clean and sober?*

Steven: I just do it. I try to hide the addiction from the kids. I wasn't aware I was doing boundaries. I never really thought about it.

Tracie: Let's think about it. Let's think about the many ways you can keep yourself safe and protected, clean and sober and how that can help your family be safe too. One of those boundaries of course is the people you mix with. They say you partly become like the six closest people to you. What about the people you mix with and surround yourself with? So what would you be like if you mixed and hung out with people taking drugs?

Steven: Still a druggy I suppose.

Tracie: What if you didn't mix with or hang out with those people? What if you actually avoided those people and deleted them from your phone? Would that be a betrayal or would you be protecting your sobriety and your wife and family? Are you or they worth that?

Steven: Yeah I reckon. It makes sense to me.

Tracie: You don't think less of those people, pity them or think you are better than them but it's simply that you've moved on in your life – big time. Previously when you have met with those drug friends it has led to you taking drugs and sometimes getting drunk. Is it time for you to grow up and become a fully mature man, being clean and sober and protecting your sobriety?

Steven: Yeah. I've got to do that, haven't I?

Tracie: And maybe you might think about staying away from your brother, at least for a while.

> *Maybe you would have stronger boundaries around being clean and sober. Does staying away from him using drugs or alcohol and places where that takes place make sense to you and is it something you will now do?*

Steven: *Sure does, Tracie. I can do that. As you say I've got to protect being clean and sober which will keep me safe and protect my wife and family. The thing is, I've now been making a lot of money again and I agreed to go back into business with my brother and his friend buying some land and building holiday cabins to let.*

Tracie: *Well Steven. I'm going to put my business hat on for a moment. How did that last venture with your brother work out?*

Steven: *A disaster.*

Tracie: *Who started you on drugs?*

Steven: *My brother.*

Tracie: *What started you on meth three years ago?*

Steven: *My brother.*

Tracie: *What does your wife think of the new scheme?*

Steven: *She's freaked out by it.*

Tracie: *How has she reacted about your taking meth?*

Steven: *She's freaked out about it.*

Jedrzejczak (2005) found three factors that increased the likelihood of addiction in families. The first is the impact of pathological families' effects on young people's behaviour; the second is easy access to drugs; and the third is influence by groups of people of the same age. People generally consider friends as part of their extended families. Family bonds, however, can be very strong and people frequently create negative hallucinations around the failings of their relatives and friends, often excusing the most destructive and even violent behaviours.

Why many treatments, both in-patient and out-patient, for addiction and alcoholism fail is because after the period of treatment, the person goes back to their social circle and environment, which for many different reasons, was part of the addiction in the first place. The cues for the addictive behaviours can be triggered in all modalities again, both consciously and unconsciously, when the client goes back to the source of addiction and where addiction may be the norm.

Step 5 – Establish Good Boundaries intentions

1. Addicts are very poor at boundaries which is how they got into trouble in the first place.
2. In recovery it is important to teach your clients to have good boundaries around living clean and sober.
3. Not only can you do this somnambulistically, but also include it in the trance work.

Step 5 – Establish Good boundaries trance script

(Tracie): Steven close your eyes and relax more in the chair (paying attention to self)… let's just imagine for a moment that the people you mix with added to your life and did not steal from it (psycho-imaginary visualisation, personal interaction sorting)… what would it be like for you to be hanging out with clean and sober people (as if frame, interrogative suggestion)…**isn't it much easier to be clean and sober** (transderivational search, deepening trance, as if frame, interrogative suggestion)…you might have thought that people who you used to take drugs or drink with were your friends (recall, placing that behaviour in the past, recontextualising, time shift)...they have to belong to your past now (direct suggestion)...**you can be selective with who you mix with** (truism, permissive suggestion, implied directive)... deleting the people from your life who don't support your clean and sober life (negative hallucination, installing boundaries)... they have their life and you have yours (suggestion for social separation)...**you can choose to be with clean and sober people** (permissive suggestion lowers resistance)...learning how to have strong boundaries in your life (direct suggestion)...implementing those boundaries daily (direct suggestion)...strong boundaries that keep you out of denial (truism)...**you will choose to be with clean and sober people each day** (post-hypnotic suggestion)... nod your head if that's OK (wait for affirmation, yes set)...will you remember that every day won't you (interrogative suggestion, confusion, grammatically incorrect hidden suggestion, wait for affirmation, yes set)...shake your head if you don't want to change your mind do you (wait for the shake of the head, no set)...you never want to go back to your old life do you (wait for the head shake, no set)...you won't allow anyone to take that sobriety away from you will you (interrogative suggestion, no set, locking the gate)...**you choose a clean and sober life always** (direct suggestion)...the people in your contacts list associated with that old life (cognitive sorting)...**deleted** (suggestion for behavioural regulator)...when you see them in the street (cognitive awareness)...**wave and walk on** (suggestion for behavioural regulation)...maintaining clear strong well defined consistent boundaries protecting your clean and sober life (direct suggestion)...you can choose (illusion of choice, behavioural bind)...**as you live your good life maintaining good boundaries** (direct suggestion, contingent suggestion, double bind).

Therapeutic boundaries

LaBay (2003) wrote about client-centred approaches in hypnotherapy. I was trained many years ago in Rogerian client-centred approaches to counselling. In an age where the client personal-centred approaches are often the buzzwords, therapists are frequently discouraged away from directing clients, instead expecting them to come up with their own solutions. This can also be driven by the fear of being sued by the client for giving them the wrong advice or sending them in the wrong direction in life.

So the question arises: How much do you as a therapist insert yourself and your ideas into the client's life, ideas and mentality? Since I work from a naturopathic perspective, I am constantly directing my clients towards a healthier life without apology. Clients know this in advance because it states so in my profile, advertising material and is explained to them during the session, so it is no surprise to them. They may not be able to comply with all my advice with regard to actions, other than stopping the addiction, but whatever they do, they are congratulated and asked to work on the rest.

We must also consider the coordinated approach that we might take and the necessary boundaries that need to be in place with other professionals involved. I will not share a client with another counsellor, psychologist, psychotherapist or psychiatrist, working therapeutically, as the client becomes confused and productivity tends to decline. My experience is when two therapists are working with the same client, it is like two chefs in the kitchen trying to prepare the same dish together at once. It will only end in disaster, because what one does, the other may undo. I am a brief therapist, so the way I work with clients is so fast that non-hypnotherapists can find it confrontational, because they may want to see the client for years, week after week.

Often family doctors try to play the therapist and get clients to take medications when I believe clients should not necessarily be on medication. In these cases I refer the client to another family doctor who understands the way I work. However, when a client has medical issues outside my experience or remit, I will refer that part of the treatment on to a specialist. All these issues are good for you to discuss in clinical supervision.

> **Tracie:** You said Steven that when you were under a psychiatrist at one point and admitted to a hospital for depression, no one suggested to you to stop taking recreational drugs.
>
> **Steven:** No they didn't think it was important or the cause of my depression. They just kept giving me more medications. They sort of expected me to get better by taking more medications.
>
> **Tracie:** Did you?
>
> **Steven:** No.
>
> **Tracie:** And you have not seen the psychiatrist for four years or been taking any medications; even though you've been taking the methamphetamine you haven't been depressed.
>
> **Steven:** When I don't take the meth, which has not been very often, I'm sort of OK. When I take the meth it does push me to the edge again. Since coming to see you and cutting out the meth I'm doing much better.
>
> **Tracie:** So are you up for doing more of doing better?
>
> **Steven:** I sure am. You bet.

Satir (1983) talked about how, in families, one person can be playing the role of the sick person and how other members of the family can try to push that person back into the role to maintain the status quo. There is also the issue of relatives or close friends being involved in the client's therapy which can, in many ways, be a double-edged sword. The addict needs all the support they can get, but I try to keep third parties out of the therapy room because they are pushing their agenda, not the agenda of the client. When the third party is not getting what they want, they can start to sabotage therapy by trying to redirect therapy to their issues, not the issues of the client.

If the third party is funding the therapy, they can pull that funding and sabotage the therapy if they personally are not getting from therapy the changes they want the client to experience.

Berne (1996) encouraged adults to change their dependent behaviours to become more mature and independent. When the person becomes too dependent on the therapist, or family or friends, they are avoiding maturing their personality and acting in a childlike way. Outside the therapy room family, friends or work colleagues can also sabotage the client's therapy when it is not fitting in with their own goals, and the client must learn to be resistant to such moves. I find it more effective to get the client to build their own support network outside the therapy room that supports them in their everyday life as clean and sober. When that support network is working well, it can accelerate and strengthen therapeutic results.

Tracie: *You said your wife is an angel. Does she support your sobriety?*

Steven: *She's a saint. Put up with all my problems for years. She loves you. Now I'm not taking meth, she wants me to put you in my tool bag, take you home and keep you in the garage.*

Tracie: *So she's a good woman?*

Steven: *The best.*

Tracie: *Of course Steven there is only one person who has made this happen. One person who has stopped taking the meth. One person who has become clean and sober. And one person who will continue to be clean and sober for the rest of your life. And since you're really getting to grips with boundaries, now one person that will make that happen every day of your life, endeavouring to keep you and your family safe.*

The Global Advertising Lawyers Alliance (2005), in reviewing the laws in many countries, found that often advertising was not supposed to espouse that alcohol had therapeutic effects, yet when you review most alcohol advertising, that is precisely what is suggested. The pharmaceutical industry spends billions of dollars per year promoting their drugs as efficacious. Illicit drug dealers market their drugs through underground networks as equally beneficial and as the answer to many of life's problems.

For some people, the use of drugs and alcohol is to seek some relief from stressful situations and circumstances. While this is not true for all addicts, many people are led to alcohol, for example, as a way to relax, and manufacturers embark on sophisticated advertising campaigns to impart this message to the public.

Since recreational drugs are not generally advertised, except as medications in North America, and when they are marketed as natural substances, mass advertising is less effective. There is, however, a whole word-of-mouth advertising that takes place with recreational drugs and many internet sites which recommend certain drugs, often driven by drug pushers as stress relief.

Sinha (2008) points out that stress is a well-known precursor to addiction and can be a major part of the withdrawal process. Stress during withdrawal from addiction can prove so challenging and distressing for many addicts to the point that in some cases the addict relapses rather than go through the initial withdrawal process. So an important part of recovery is teaching the client to be able to relax and access peaceful states through the use of the mind, therefore settling the mind and the body.

> Tracie: *You've had a lot of ups and down in your life Steven starting with your brother introducing you to drugs which clouded your ability to make good judgements; your experience with the com-*

pany going bankrupt after the financial collapse; the major depression that followed that loss of money and humiliation you felt; your time being admitted to a psychiatric hospital; the past years of taking meth virtually every day, leading to losing your ability to get an erection; and finally you are proposing to follow your brother into yet another venture.

Steven: Yeah I suppose he's a bit of dickhead and I guess I've got to start doing this boundaries stuff you're talking about.

Tracie: You know there are no guarantees in life. I can't promise you everything will be perfect in the future. Stuff happens and that's life. Throughout life there will be disasters. The only thing I can promise you is that life changes constantly and one of the great secrets of life is to be able to be calm when that happens and adapt with the changes. In other words you could be calm enough to deal with any changes. Do you think being able to do that might be useful for you?

Steven: Well my wife would be surprised but I think it might help me.

Hypnotherapists are trained in many different ways so I have included in this chapter on boundaries guidance on how to help the client manage stress. It is my experience that unless a therapist develops these skills in the recovering addict, the client may well revert to addiction when encountering stress that they were not previously equipped to handle. Our job is not to release the stress for the client but to teach them to be able to release their own out-of-control or inappropriate stress.

Lily leaf intention

1. It is important for you to be able to teach the client to create a deeply relaxed state as their body may be exhausted from addiction.
2. Relaxation, plus a sense of peace and calm, is essential for recovery, both physically and mentally, from addiction. The client needs to be able to create this hypnotic state quickly and on cue.

Lily leaf trance script

(Tracie): Take a moment to close your eyes and go inside go inside Steven (re-induction)...go deep...deeper...all the way inside yourself (deepener)...**the outside world doesn't matter for a while** (negative hallucination for Ve, Ae, Ke, Oe, Ge, trance deepener)...you are all alone (sensory deprivation suggestion)... no one else around...**right in the centre of your being** (trance deepener)...perhaps there is a pond or a lake (positive hallucination)...quite magical and far far away (kinaesthetic internal good feeling)...in the centre you might find a giant lily leaf (transderivational search)...**everything is so still and quiet** (catatonia)... any outside noises you might hear send you deeper into that place (contingent suggestion for trance deepening)...the water is still...the air lovely (kinaesthetic internal good feelings)...you are calmer with each slow long breath (contingent suggestion)... **full of peace...calm...deep relaxation** (suggestion for a sense of well-being)...you will remember this place and any time you get stressed you can stop what you are doing and remember (arrestation of panic response, post-hypnotic suggestion for recall of well-being state at the onset of stress, adaptive behaviour suggestion, Pavlovian response)...go to one side and visit this place again (positive hallucination)...wherever you go that place goes with you inside (suggestion for generalised resources)...**taking a moment and going inside sitting on the large lily leaf** (positive hallucination)…and instantly your cares will drift away for a while (negative hallucination)…**full of peace**…**calm**…**deep relaxation** (state changing)…and when you wake up you can handle the situation calmly (post-hypnotic suggestion for coping skills)…one step at a time (suggestion for chunking)…you can bring that back with you (post-hypnotic suggestion for generalised resource transference)… **peace**…**calm**…**deep relaxation** (state changing)…back with you to life with your eyes open and smiling at me (somnambulism).

State shifting

State shifting is teaching clients to shift their physical, mental and emotional state quickly and at times immediately. State shifting is a fundamental hypnotherapy practice I use with all my clients, although not always around simulated drug-induced states, yet I rarely see it taught in hypnotherapy schools. To teach clients state shifting, the therapist must not only be able to do this themselves but also demonstrate to the client that they can do it, so the client can model them. Many therapists are afraid of not looking professional or appearing less than proper when they demonstrate state shifting. There is a great deal of paranoia around personal disclosure by therapists of their own experiences and abilities to clients that is unnecessary and bourgeois.

For a recovering addict to maintain their boundaries, it is important that in becoming clean and sober they do not feel they have had their experiences constrained, stolen or that they have been deprived in some way. Addicts do not generally understand that many of the experiences they have on drugs can be replicated simply with the mind and imagination.

State shifting is a series of skills that sets hypnotherapy apart from other therapies because it seeks to change the client's state fast and not necessarily wait for the client to experience intellectual enlightenment about their own situation. Indeed, it is partly a form of somatic therapy because it is paying attention to the physical state of the body in addition to changing the mental and emotional states.

In the documentary *Mevlana and the Whirling Dance* (Weibel, 2014) we see the Whirling Dervishes, inspired by the Persian poet Rumi, who spin hundreds of times during their ceremonial performance, attaining a state of ecstasy in an altered state of awareness. The average person would fall down after a few spins but the practised dancer continues to spin hundreds of times while maintaining their balance.

Parwha & Khalsa (1998) show us how, for thousands of years, yogic practices have been helping people change their physical, mental and emotional states through breathing and meditation. Some of those practices such as the 'Breath of Fire' are not soporific and involve altered states of hyperventilation, great excitement, energy and feelings of ecstasy.

Kataria (1999), accredited with making laughter yoga popular, demonstrated state-changing from depression to happiness through breathing practices and focusing the mind on what helps us laugh on a daily basis. When practised in groups, the laughter and inducting of the happy state becomes even more infectious and is now practised as a daily ritual in many places in India at the beginning of each school day.

Spanos (1996) saw hypnosis as a form of dissociation, saying it was when we left our normal state of consciousness and at times under the control of an alter personality. At times that dissociation suggested pathology occurred when some people entered into a form of multiple personality, giving rise to false memories. The problem, however, with academic research is its observations are often based on too narrow a hypothesis that fails to consider wider possibilities or perspectives.

My opinion is that hypnosis and accessing altered states of awareness through hypnosis opens doorways to human experience. Some of those memories of experiences of altered states of awareness are in our unconscious library that we can recall and re-experience. Those experiences, which are not normally available, can be utilised in a therapeutic manner upon recall and recreation. It also opens up the immense power of the imagination, ignited and directed by suggestion, to experience states that the addict used to experience under the influence of their drug of choice.

As hypnotherapists, we should not be bound by dogma, and while we need to study therapy during training, simply trying to do therapy by numbers restricts the art of therapy. We can seek to guide our clients to ever new experiences, and in the case of recovering from addiction, to attain altered states of awareness when clean and sober. While people in altered states may shift from one alter personality to another, that in itself is a natural state of functioning, and not necessarily pathological.

The body experiences an emotional topography of living that is meant to be vastly diverse in nature. Humans and other animals have a full emotional spectrum that ranges from being soporific and practically comatose to heightened elation. Addicts can be afraid of feeling flat when they are not taking the addictive substances and they equate that to being a boring person and being bored. Because they have relied on a chemical aid to change their experiences, they have partly lost the ability that humans have to change their own emotional states on cue. State shifting comes from yogic traditions of changing human experience through breathing and meditation. Since in hypnotherapy we add hypnotic suggestion, the changes can happen very quickly.

Tracie: *Are you having a good time today Steven?*

Steven: *Yeah. I suppose I'm learning a lot of stuff?*

Tracie: *Isn't it interesting that you are having a good time and not taking any drugs or alcohol? Isn't it interesting that you have not taken anything for*

two weeks and you are having a good time?
So what are you learning? How come you can
take no drugs or alcohol and have a good time?
Well that answer is very easy because your mind
and your body have the ability to create any
experience you would like instantly.

Steven: *So like I'm doing drugs but not doing drugs?*

Tracie: *That's a very good way of putting it. You're learning to experience all those things while staying
clean, sober and safe.*

Steven: *Can I do that?*

Tracie: *I'll teach you.*

The buzz – Hypnosis in high beta brain wave state for stimulant addicts intentions

1. People who have experienced the very high energy states induced by amphetamines often miss that high on withdrawal. That longing to experience those states can lead to relapses.
2. Teaching people to replicate those highs through hypnotic elevated states of awareness and euphoria when they want to can lead to reduced relapses. We can see these states being created traditionally by the Whirling Dervishes.
3. There is a need to teach the client to create both the physical and mental experiences of that heightened altered state of awareness.

The buzz – Hypnosis in high beta brain wave state for stimulant addicts trance script

OK so you liked speed, amphetamines (truism)…the thing is they no longer physically like you (separation of the person and the drug)…**your body can't take those drugs anymore** (truism, direct suggestion)…sometimes however you might like to go and party or dance until late (indirect suggestion to re-experience the state sober)…and why would anyone not (permission for altered state of awareness)…you can of course create your own energy clean and sober (indirect suggestion)…**so would you like that buzz** (interrogative suggestion)…OK follow me let's stand up (modelling)…I want you to remember a time when you were off your face (regression to state of hyper-alertness)… high as a kite (fractionation)…**make your breathing faster now** (changing bodily experiences)…higher up in your head (increasing alertness and hyperventilation)…that's right faster still (fractionation)…keep that breathing fast and high in your head (direct suggestion)…**your body becomes energised** (direct suggestion)… let's move around and bust some moves (physical stimulation)… that energy comes over you in waves and rushes (direct suggestion)…**again and again and again** (fractionation)…feel that light-headedness (inducing altered state of awareness)…your whole body keeps moving (modelling the effects of stimulants)… you have no cares for a while (removing critical resistance)…your eyes become very wide with your pupils dilated (modelling the effects of stimulants)…it's like you can see everything all at once (hyper-vigilance)…**faster breathing** (fractionation)…**energised light-headedness** (increasing heart rate)…**can't keep your body still** (modelling the effects of stimulants)…**eyes wide**…go for it…you're confident…you love everyone (increased sense of freedom)…**and times it by 10 now** (fractionation)…good hey…**times it by 100** (fractionation)…have a nice one…stay with it and enjoy and come down when you want to…

Steven had a life-long history of taking recreational drugs. On top of that, he had spent time taking psychiatric drugs but his addiction to recreational drugs had never been addressed. Since his early years his brother had led him into one bad situation after another. Because of his unquestioning loyalty to his brother, he had never really examined where that had led him or the effects it had had on his family. Instead of the intense guidance, counselling and therapy such a young man would need after a crisis, he was given more drugs that did not solve any of his problems. When I first saw him, he was flying into Sydney for five days a week from another city, working 16 hours a day running a crew of four other carpenters, making a lot of money and taking methamphetamine to keep up that momentum.

He stopped using drugs after the first session, decided not to go back into business with his brother and to cut contact with him until he no longer took drugs, despite his parents' disapproval of this decision. He also decided after the current contract was finished he was going to work nearer his home and spend more time with his family. I saw him for four sessions in total, during which we also addressed the erectile dysfunction that had occurred as the result of the drug addiction and over-exposure to stress.

Here are some other state-shifting techniques for different types of addiction:

Space cadet – Hypnosis for inducing an altered state of euphoria for heroin and opioid addicts intentions

1. Heroin and opiate users report a state of awareness that is euphoric, warm and cocoon-like. It is a state of semi-consciousness where the user goes inside into an alternate reality. This is a place where the user feels safe.

2. Heroin users have difficulty coping with the real world and at times seek a respite from reality. If they can do this without drugs, this can ease their transition to sobriety.

3. You can teach your client to do that hypnotically for brief periods to give them stress relief, so that they cope better with everyday life.

Space cadet – Hypnosis in an altered state of euphoria for heroin and opioid addicts trance script

Let's go to that place of euphoria you know (addicts carry their memories of the altered states of awareness they have experienced)…imagine if your body was safe and your mind was creative as you are clean and sober (safe equals clean and sober and the mind has the ability to induce an altered state of awareness itself)…**you can keep your eyes open and look at me as you go into that state of euphoria** (permission to experience the state legitimately in everyday life)…let your pupils shrink now as the world outside does not become so important (opioids cause sensory dissociation)…suddenly you feel so safe (modelling the feelings that opioids produce)…**your breathing slows down** (trance deepener)…everything is OK (suggestion that it is OK to be sober and have a good time)…everything is love (acceptance of altered state)…**you can let go** (a learning experience of being able to enjoy without drugs)…it feels warm and comfortable (modelling how opioid addicts describe their experience)…**time is not important** (dissociation)…you feel warm and comfortable (fractionation)… the world is rosy (modelling how opioid addicts describe their experience)…you're on a cloud just floating along (external sensory withdrawal)…**you feel really good naturally enjoying that euphoria** (associating feeling good with being clean and sober)… stay in that place floating for a while (permission to feel good and have no sense of urgency)…as long as you like inside your mind (time distortion)…just giving in to those good feelings (surrendering to sobriety)…**and when you come back bring some of them with you** (transference of desired feelings to the sober state, partial or total somnambulism, post- and intra-hypnotic suggestion).

Smashed – Fun on endorphins, dopamine and serotonins for cannabis addicts intentions

1. Users of cannabis experience both a relaxed state and a state of

experiencing fun, depending on why they are using the drug.

2. Constant use of those drugs makes the brain lazy and it ceases to produce sufficient serotonin and endorphins.
3. You need to teach the client hypnotically to create those states naturally.

Smashed – Fun on endorphins, dopamine and serotonins for cannabis addicts trance script

Sometimes it's OK to play (giving permission to experience being stoned)…I'm sure you would agree (ratification that experience will change)…sometime it's fun to see the world differently (initiation of perceptual change)…**and when you look at things they can be interesting** (cannabis users can be focused on specific stimuli)…you're chilled yet amused (state recall)… maybe I look odd or funny (sensory alteration)…highly comical (everyone finds other people's idiosyncrasies funny but we can only laugh at them in an altered state)…**perhaps you might want to laugh a little** (emulating laughter yoga techniques)... more than that (fractionation)…and even more…it's OK to get lost in the moment (modelling the time disorientation that happens when being stoned)…colours can become more intense (hypersensitivity)…almost as if things are swirling around (disorientation)…you get lost in your thoughts for a while (internal sensory focus)…**now you want to laugh…and laugh and laugh again** (fractionation)…everything's so chilled and funny (creating good feelings and bridging them to being clean and sober)… **you're having such a good time in your mind naturally** (direct suggestion)…things get so funny you just have to sit down and give into it (suggestion for relaxation)…wow don't you just love getting out of it naturally (ratification of trance state)…

Chapter 9 References

Berne, E. (1996). *Games people play: The basic handbook of transactional analysis.* New York, NY: Ballantine Books.

Campbell, S. F. (Ed.). 1976. *Piaget sampler: An introduction to Jean Piaget through his own words.* New York, NY: John Wiley & Sons.

DeCasien, A. R., Williams, S. A., & Higham, J. P. (in press). Primate brain size is predicted by diet but not sociality. *Nature Ecology & Evolution.* doi:10.1038/s41559-017-0112

Global Advertising Lawyers Alliance. (2015). *Alcohol advertising: A global legal perspective.* New York, NY: Author.

Hansen, W. B., & Graham, J. W. (1991). Preventing alcohol, marijuana, and cigarette use among adolescents: Peer pressure resistance training versus establishing conservative norms. *Preventative Medicine, 20*(3), 414–430.

Jedrzejczak, M. (2005). Family and environmental factors of drug addiction among young recruits. *Military Medicine, 170*(8), 688–690.

Kataria, M. (1999). *Laugh for no reason.* Mumbai, India: Madhuri International.

Katherine, A. (1994). *Boundaries: Where you end and I begin— How to recognize and set healthy boundaries.* Center City, MN: Hazelden.

LaBay, M. L. (2003). *Hypnotherapy: A client-centered approach.* Grenta, LA: Pelican.

Parwha, S., & Khalsa, K. (1998). *Kundalini yoga: The flow of eternal power.* New York, NY: Perigee.

Satir, V. (1983). *Conjoint family therapy* (3rd ed.). Palo Alto, CA: Science and Behavior Books.

Sinha, R. (2008). Chronic stress, drug use and vulnerability to addiction. *Annals of the New York Academy of Sciences, 1141,* 105–130. doi:10.1196/annals.1441.030

Spanos, N. P. (1996). *Multiple identities and false memories: A sociocognitive perspective.* Washington, D. C.: American Psychological Association.

Weibel, B. [Barbara Weibel]. (2014, January 18). *Mevlevi sema ceremony (Sufi whirling dervishes) in Istanbul* [Video file]. Retrieved from https://www.youtube.com/watch?v=vvmzY2gtRVQ

10 *Being an Emissary*

The sixth final step of recovering from drug and alcohol addiction is the journey of transformation. The addict who just stops taking their substance of abuse is simply an addict who has stopped taking their substance of abuse. They are not someone who is clean and sober. It would be easy to say that addiction is different for everyone and the client must find their own way of living, but relapses happen for addicts when they have not fundamentally changed their personalities. It is the personality that is the addict, not the body.

The *DSM-5* (American Psychiatric Association, 2013) classifies addictions as diseases but there is no evidence of a physiological cause of addiction. Giving people the label of having a disease disempowers them during recovery because it positions the client as a victim so they adopt a victim mentality and abandon self-agency. No one can recover from addiction without a strong sense of self-agency.

Tracie: *I want to say to you Beth that over the past two weeks you have not taken heroin because you decided not to take heroin. I want you to take the full credit for that because after the first time I saw you, it was you who changed what you do.*

Beth: *I couldn't have done it without you.*

Tracie: *You can do anything you choose in this life. Of course, people tell you that when you are young*

> *but few people ever listen to that message. Most people don't discover they could have done anything they wanted until they become older and some people never do. You've now learnt that lesson at the ripe old age of 22...congratulations.*

Beth: *It was a weird four years. I was so full of hopes and dreams at university, then I started taking heroin when I met my boyfriend, dropped out of my course and lived on welfare. I hated my life. I hated what I became. I hated myself.*

Tracie: *You've become clean and sober and what's not to like in that? What's not to like in you taking back control over your life? What's not to like in that you are only 22 years old and have your whole life in front of you? How exciting is that?*

Beth: *I suppose it is, isn't it?*

Tracie: *You suppose very well, although I would question the use of the word 'boyfriend'.*

Beth: *Yes, with him still using and me not, it looks like we're at the end of our relationship.*

Part of a transformational journey is the end of one part of a person's life and the beginning of another. We cannot hold on to the past, who we were or what we were doing. As an organism, we are always transforming and adapting. The journey of the self is life itself and as humans we are compelled to change.

Tracie: *Step 6 is becoming an emissary. An emissary is an ambassador of the way you live your life clean and sober. You might not run up to someone on the street and tell them you are clean and*

> *sober, but the way you act, hold yourself and live*
> *tells each person you meet that's the way your*
> *life is: clean and sober.*

Beth: *Is that forever? Can't I even drink again?*

Tracie: *Let me ask you this: You're in a room, the room is*
on fire and all you have is a bottle of gin. What do
you do?

Beth: *Two weeks ago I would have said 'drink the gin'*
but I guess I don't drink gin anymore.

Tracie: *Wear your sobriety with pride. You've earned it.*
It makes you strong. Let it shine out of your eyes.
Be a model for others.

Swami Vishnu-Devananda (1999) tells us that meditation and mantras have been used in India and Asia for thousands of years. The yogi gives the person a mantra to say over and over again throughout the day as a form of mental programming, even though it is presented, at times, as a spiritual correction.

Willey (2014) informs us that the Chinese philosopher Confucius gave rise to Confucianism by laying down a doctrine which led to a way of living according to the philosophy of his teachings. Bukkyō Dendō Kyōkai (1995) presents the teachings of the Buddha by which millions of people live their lives across the globe today. Religions such as the Catholic Church use the same kind of indoctrination and mind control through mechanisms like the catechisms, prayers and the Hail Mary (US Catholic Church, 1992). *The Jewish Prayer Book* presents pathways of adoration, ideology and codes of self-regulation (Anonymous, 2015). Ali (1992) sets out the regulation of Muslim prayers according to the teachings of the Quran that guides a Muslim's way of living. Coue (2006) promoted his method of auto-suggestion as a form of mind self-programming and reprogramming to help people change their behaviours.

So it is not a great stretch of the imagination that we, as hypnotists and therapists, can have the ability to help the client program their mind to live as clean and sober for the rest of their life. If you as the therapist live your life clean and sober, your teachings become a powerful influence in the client's life because you are congruent with the life you are asking the client to lead.

Tracie: Let's talk about what being an emissary is because it comes as a whole package. It's, of course, not just about not taking drugs or alcohol. That would just be someone who has given something up. It's about you embracing a way of living that is clean of body, healthy and vibrant. Do you feel more healthy and vibrant now?

Beth: Physically I'm getting there. I know it's the right path for me.

Tracie: You know you can't go back, don't you?

Beth: I know, and I don't want to.

Tracie: You know going forward is about you being extremely healthy in body, mind and the way you live, don't you?

Beth: I do.

Tracie: Do you deserve that?

Beth: I do.

Tracie: Don't want to change your mind?

Beth: No.

Tracie: Don't want to slip backwards for the occasional fix?

Beth: No. What if someone asks me why I don't drink or take drugs?

Tracie: *You don't have to tell everyone you meet, but if someone asks, be honest if it feels right. Tell them you used to have problems but you no longer do. Tell them you are clean and sober and proud of yourself. Show them that you are an emissary and ambassador for a clean and sober, healthy way of living.*

Step 10 – Being an Emissary intentions

It is important for the client to be living the clean and sober life happily and with celebration.

1. Shame is a great saboteur for the addict, causing relapses. When the client does not have to hide who they are and what they once were, this empowers them further to embrace a clean and sober life.
2. When a client can say they are not an active addict, it empowers them to re-identify with the identity they have now of being clean and sober.
3. Being an emissary for the clean and sober life allows the client to have a sense of altruism, and altruism is one of the strongest drivers for staying clean and sober.

Step 10 – Being an Emissary trance script
(Tracie): Close your eyes Beth and I want you to know how wonderful your progress has been (ego-strengthening)…you are changing which is a very honourable journey (truism, ego-strengthening, appealing to the super-ego)…**you are becoming someone quite different** (truism, intra-hypnotic suggestion, post-hypnotic suggestion, ego-strengthening, future pacing)…the quality of your life has already…**has already changed** (ratification of change)…a great deal (phonological ambiguity, confirmation of achievement, generalised suggestion for remaining clean and sober)…close your

eyes and look up inside your head (visualisation, creating alter-ego and higher self)…**you are an emissary for being clean and sober** (multiple time frame suggestion, ideal imagery, Vi good image)… you are healthier happier stronger looking good (cognitive overload, generalised direct suggestion)…it's a one way journey (closing the gate)…**this is your life now and in the future** (closing the gate, future pacing)…as you stay out of denial all the time always remembering Step 1 awake or asleep (contingent suggestion, post-hypnotic suggestion)…**you know with every part of you living clean and sober is a beautiful way to live for you** (transderivational search, direct suggestion)…everywhere you go you are an emissary for being clean and sober (suggestion for multiple location successful behaviour)…if someone asks you why you don't drink or take drugs (rehearsing difficult scenarios)…It's OK for you to be honest and say (relieving the fear of exposure of their past)…**I'm clean and sober** (post-hypnotic suggestion)…**that's really OK isn't it** (interrogative suggestion, yes set)…you can be proud with each and every breath being clean and sober for life (contingent suggestion, direct suggestion)… every day is a new day (truism) every breath a new chance to live (truism)…free to live a good life (dissolving resistance)…**you are an emissary for the clean and sober life now** (direct suggestion)… strong healthy beautiful happy always remembering (cognitive overload)…**you are the emissary for being clean and sober every day** (direct suggestion).

The majority of sickness, illness, disease and addiction that fill our hospitals and doctors' surgeries are the result of the poor lifestyles people lead. They also suffer from the neurosis induced by living in an industrial and post-industrial artificial society where people are divorced from their bodies. Schlosser (2001) shows us how the food industry has created a raft of illnesses that humans did not generally experience before the emergence of convenience food. Campbell and Campbell (2016) showed the emergence of diabetes and cancer that spread across China as the Western diet arrived. Erasmus (1999) explains how we have taken fats and heated, frozen and corrupted them to the point where they are carcinogenic, all of which affects the way the brain and hormonal systems work in the body.

Sarris and Wardle (2010) teach us that from a naturopathic perspective, the body generally has the ability to heal itself, given the right circumstances. We can see this when we look at cases such as previously mentioned Janette Murray-Wakelin (2013) who was diagnosed with metastatic cancer and given six months to live. She moved to a more natural, raw, vegan lifestyle and took up regular marathon running. Fifteen years later she ran 366 marathons in consecutive days across Australia. Literature is full of thousands of similar cases.

The addict has damaged their body during their addiction, some of which may be repairable, and some that is not. We do, however, have a duty as clinicians to guide our clients towards healthy living that is compellingly more attractive than the addiction. To do that, we must be embodying healthy living our-selves. We must allow the client to model us, as they have come to us to teach them to live better lives. For some clients, who have suffered brain damage, hepatitis C and HIV infection, liver or kidney failure, we must help them to manage their situation the best that they can or refer them on to specialists.

Tracie: *At 22 Beth you are still young. You have so much life ahead of you; people to meet, places to go, adventures to live. And being clean and sober for you is a gateway to all of those things. I'm so ex-cited for you. You now have the power to make that happen. Are you excited?*

Beth: *I am.*

Tracie: *I'm excited for you too. When I think of all the adventures I've had in my life between your age*

and mine, it's been wonderful and can be wonderful for you too as you take control of your life
as you go forward and shape it in ways that are
right for you and right for those around you in
the right place. Is that all right?

Beth: Yes.

Tracie: You will always remember to live by the clean
and sober way of living. When you encounter
drugs and alcohol, you move away to a safe
space for you. What other people do is their
business and what you do is yours. You maintain
and re-enforce your clean and sober way of
living throughout your life and it helps you have
a great life...because you make it so.

Beth: I will.

Tracie: As I teach everyone life begins in your body.
When you take care of your body your body
takes care of you. Eat a plant-based diet. It gives
you energy and keeps your body clean. Exercise
regularly every week. The exercise helps you let
go of stress. It raises your level of serotonin and
endorphins which is raising your happiness level.
And it's increasing dopamine which helps your
nervous system work well. And this is a win,
win, win life isn't it?

Beth: Yes.

Tracie: Did I tell you about my Great Aunt who was
diagnosed with terminal cancer in 1939 and
told she had three months to put her affairs into
order? Well she refused to listen and lived to be
101 years old. Did I tell you about an old drunk

tramp I used to see on the streets of Mayfair in London for decades, then one day I saw her on the television and she looked completely different? The man interviewing her asked her why she changed her life and she simply said she got fed up with the old life. People change. Have you changed now here today?

Beth: I have.

Tracie: Have you become clean and sober for life?

Beth: Yes I have.

Tracie: You see it doesn't need 26 therapy sessions to help you. Or years out of your life that you waste. I don't need to know all the reasons you ended up a heroin addict. All I need to know is have you changed and become clean and sober for life?

Beth: Yes I have for life.

In all the work I do as a therapist with people recovering from drug and alcohol addiction, I am looking for a change of the person's belief system to support their change in behaviour and new lifestyle. Dilts, Halbom, and Smith (2012) proposed that in order for the body to change and maintain that change made through hypnotic interactions, the client's belief system must change. Not only can you as a hypnotist suggest a change of beliefs to the client, but you also need to check that change has taken place and that the change is robust.

Rossi (1993), in looking at the change of the physical self at microbiological levels, found that suggestion and changes of cognition do, in actual fact, change the physiological state. We know this from studying the effects of stress on the onset of cancer, adrenal function, glucose metabolism, immune suppression, gastrointestinal dysfunction, and suppression of production of serotonin, dopamine and endorphins. As hypnotherapists, we also know that often this biological dysfunction can be reversed through the use of suggestion in hypnosis. The values underline the beliefs that strengthen the ego, allowing it to regulate the desires and demands of the id, under the guidance of the superego.

Tracie: Hey Beth I'd like to tell you a story. Do you like stories?

Beth: I do.

Tracie: Good...well it's not a made-up story but actually a real story of something that really happened. So it's really real and has a great ending. Many years ago I spent time with someone who was coming off heroin just like you. They had had a rotten time and tried before to come off heroin and they wanted a better life. They had a pretty low opinion of themselves and didn't believe they could achieve anything much. Previously they had not believed they could live without heroin, like many addicts do. They were quite surprised that I spent the time with them and that I believed they could be clean and sober. The thing is though when you hang out with people for quite a while you begin to believe some of the things they do. Have you ever found that?

Beth: Yes I have. I began to believe some of that shit my boyfriend believes.

Tracie: Well the surprise is that beginning to believe in the future is even stronger when it is about positive things. In fact when you practise *believing positive things you really increase the odds of those things coming true. Anyway, I have this belief that people are basically smart most of the time, have good intentions and given the right opportunities, which they can make for themselves, will flourish in life. Sure, life changes and we have to adapt but I believe that we can adapt very quickly. So that person who hung out with me began to believe in themselves and that belief grew stronger and stronger and stronger. They really started believing they can live a good life clean and sober and that it was in fact the easiest and most rewarding way to live. Just like you're believing now aren't you?*

Beth: *Yes I am.*

Tracie: *Well that was 20 years ago. And sometimes I hear from that person and they still believe in their clean and sober life, happy and strong. They've believed that for a long time now and they seem to be having a great life with their loving family. What they believed of course is in themselves and their ability to create a fabulous life being clean and sober all the time. Do you have that belief now?*

Beth: *I do.*

Tracie: *Is that a really strong belief?*

Beth: *It is.*

Tracie: *How really really really strong and is it for life?*

Beth: *It's forever and really really really really strong.*

What we now know is that the brain as well as the body can dramatically recover from trauma and diseases, given the right circumstances. However, those circumstances must be very specific. Naturopaths follow three principles: weed, seed and feed. Weed is the removal of toxins, inflammatory influences and circumstances that proliferate the growth of bacteria, viruses and other micro-organisms. It is also the removal of influences that retards the body's ability to heal, which not only includes drugs and alcohol, but also toxins and non-life enhancing influences such as poor food choices and stress. Gutman (2008) teaches us the body's greatest detoxifier is glutathione, which promotes nerve tissue repair. We cannot take it as a supplement because it has a very short life so we must create the circumstances to promote production of glutathione.

Tracie: *You've been detoxing over the past two weeks but your body still holds many toxins that it needs to get rid of as you get better so your body and nerves can return to a healthy state of being. Also those toxins hide in the fat in your body and are slowly released. Foods that will help this are arugula, bok choy, broccoli, Brussels sprouts, cabbage, cauliflower, collard greens and kale. And of course eating them raw accelerates that detoxification.*

Beth: *I've been doing some of the stuff in shakes and juicing like you asked me. I've even had wheatgrass each day.*

Tracie: *That's brilliant. You also need to eat as much raw fruit and vegetables as you can. And lots of greens.*

Beth: *So like vegetarian full time?*

Tracie: *Even more than that. Your body has been starved of nutrition for so long. That's why heroin addicts often look like zombies. We need to fill your body with good vitamins and minerals, so eating a high raw-food, plant-based diet is the best way to get your body to health fast. I'm going to give you information on lots of books you can read.*

Beth: *Will I get enough protein?*

Tracie: *That's a really good question and the one that most people ask. You'll get as much protein as a gorilla, hippopotamus, or elephant. Your energy will be higher and you will sleep like a baby. Most importantly your body will heal and strengthen faster.*

Beth: *That will be nice. It's been a long time since life has been like that for me.*

Tracie: *You're 22 years old. According to what you have told me there is no reason you should not make a full recovery and lead a fabulous life.*

Alexander (2010) proposes that the ever-growing problem of global addiction is due to the disenfranchisement of people from their roots and tribes. Rather than addiction being an individual problem, it is a systemic fault of an ever faster-moving society where people are often left without the support of their loved ones and kinfolk who were traditional regulators of behaviour and emotional support in times of need. He believes it is a much wider problem than drug and alcohol addiction. He suggests that mass addiction is not necessarily the sign of a decadent society, but one of a collapsing society where human needs are not being met.

We can see from my previous discussions on the attitudes of Portugal, Holland and some of the Scandinavian countries towards addiction that resocialisation into society decreases addiction relapses. This is particularly because it reduces crim-inalisation and stigmatisation, helping the addict to reintegrate back into society, thereby supporting their sobriety. A non-using addict supported by non-substance abusing people is less likely to relapse.

Addiction is a lonely place of isolation, even though an addict may mix with other addicts and even have a large social circle. It is a place where society has rejected the addict and labelled them with character flaws and undesirable traits. In helping someone become clean and sober, it is important to get them socialising once again with people who will support, not sabotage, their sobriety. The new life needs to be more emotionally attractive than the addiction. Healthy and rewarding social interactions are one of the strongest attractions that help the addict stay clean and sober. We, as hypnotists, need to firmly implant those post-hypnotic suggestions that will guide the client to continually engage in a social world.

Tracie: *Over the past four years Beth you have lived in a sort of alternative reality. It was a world where your main focus was scoring the next fix, living on planet heroin. Would you say that was true?*

Beth: *So true.*

Tracie: *You know that's not real don't you? You know that you are coming back to live with the rest of us who live in a world of friends, colleagues, partners and children don't you? We are quite nice you know and you will have a really good time. You will build a world where you have friends who don't take drugs or get drunk. Good friends. Is that OK?*

Beth: *Yes that'll be nice. I've missed just having mates I can chat to.*

Tracie:	You can rebuild your life and social network now. You can build and enjoy wholesome relationships. Connecting with people and having fun. Lots of fun. You might even connect with some of your old friends you haven't seen for years. Wouldn't that be fun? A chance to re-start your life again, this time clean and sober. A wholesome life with friends who support your sobriety. Building a new family and network around you. I'm so excited for you. Twenty-two years old with all those great times ahead of you. How excited are you?
Beth:	When you put it like that, it sounds amazing.
Tracie:	It is and will be because you make it so.

One of the most important parts of recovering from disasters in life is to mark the juncture at which people leave their past disasters behind them so they can create a new future, and this includes addiction. In my book *Inspiration for Survive and Prosper* (O'Keefe, 2013) I talk a great deal about the importance of ceremonies that we experience as human beings: christenings, bar mitzvahs, graduation, weddings and funerals.

In Alcoholics Anonymous and Narcotics Anonymous self-help movements, people get various sobriety buttons, coins, tokens or medals to celebrate the number of hours, days, months or years they have been clean and sober (Alcoholics Anonymous World Services, 2013). This allows people to have a sense of pride in their achievement of becoming clean and sober. It is a demarcation ceremony that congratulates the person and starts them on the journey to achieving their next medal.

Clients need to have a sense of their own achievements. It is ego-strengthening and raises serotonin, endorphins and dopamine. Celebrating their achievement aligns their emotional attachment to staying clean and sober and helps break the emotional attachment to the addictive substances. What we are also doing here is celebrating and creating good emotions around having been in therapy and ratifying that it worked out for them.

> Tracie: Do you think you have done well in therapy so far Beth?
>
> Beth: Well I haven't taken anything for two weeks.
>
> Tracie: How is it?
>
> Beth: I'm getting used to it.
>
> Tracie: A good used to it or other?
>
> Beth: It's the best it's been in a long time. I'm still getting used to it.
>
> Tracie: When will you be used to it? Will now be OK? Only I'm getting older and the funny thing is when you get to my age you just don't want to have to wait around for anything. You sort of want things straight away – instantly. Like instantly now? Can you be used to being clean and sober now?
>
> Beth: Yes I can.
>
> Tracie: One of the best things in life is to celebrate your successes because you've earned them. You've done really well. You worked very well in therapy. You've become clean and sober. You have become your own heroine of a better kind.

Graduation ceremony intention

1. It is important at the end of any therapy to seal therapy so the client has a sense that they have come to a point of having achieved their goals.

2. It is also important for the client to be very pleased with their progress as this increases their sense of self-efficacy and ego state.
3. Sealing therapy reduces relapses as it says to the client that they now have the skills to manage their lives themselves.
4. The graduation ceremony is a time shift for the client in that it is sealing off the traumas of the past and focusing their attention in the present time and future pacing them to perform sobriety in the future.

Graduation ceremony trance script

(Tracie): Perhaps with your eyes closed Beth you can acknowledge your success (contingent suggestion for trance and celebration of the client's progress)…seeing up inside your mind you on a stage looking good (positive hallucination, visual internal positive image)…**honoured on your journey as clean and sober** (ego-strengthening)…each part of you gets a certificate (parts resolution, ego-strengthening)…gold medals for being clean and sober (ego-strengthening)…**graduating to your new life as clean and sober** (acknowledging success)…of course it's forever (future pacing)…and you are the hero of your own journey (suggestion for self-agency, self-efficacy)…**seeing, hearing and feeling yourself as clean and sober for eternity and a day** (hallucination Vi+, Ai+, Ki+, future pacing, strategies for unconscious and conscious control)…no exceptions…not going back…no day off (closing the gate)…**clean and sober is your way of life now** (direct suggestion, present tense belief and behavioural ratification)…no matter what others do (maturation of personality, independent behaviour)…**you stay your course as clean and sober** (intra-hypnotic suggestion, post-hypnotic suggestion)…and above all it is the pride that gets you every time (future pacing Ki+)…the sheer joy of your achievement (Ki+)…**you will live clean and sober for the rest of your life** (post-hypnotic suggestion)…opening your eyes and looking at me smiling wide (somnambulism, bringing back the Ki+).

During this book I have talked about the client maturing their personality to become a self-governing, independent adult. This does not take a lifetime, nor does it take many therapy sessions. You suggest and test that this has happened as you take the client through the 6-Step Stop Drugs and Alcohol Clinical Hypnotherapy Program. Remember, the test of how effective therapy has been is how well the client functions when they have left our care.

I never saw Beth again. I was due to see her four weeks later but she rang up and cancelled with my assistant, saying she had moved. Five years later I got a surprise letter from her. She told me the day after the second session she left her boyfriend, who was still on drugs, and moved 2,000 miles away to the other side of the country. She had not used drugs or alcohol, had met a new man who she really liked, got married, had two small, beautiful, healthy children and was studying part-time at university. Even though I had only seen her twice, she said those sessions had completely changed her life. She was very grateful and wanted to tell me how things were going. Ahhh … the moments a therapist lives for.

Chapter 10 References

Alcoholics Anonymous World Services, Inc. (2013). *Dr. Bob and the good oldtimers*. New York, NY: Author.

Alexander, B. (2010). *The globalisation of addiction: A study in poverty of the spirit*. Oxford, United Kingdom: Oxford University Press.

Ali, M. M. (1992). *The Muslim prayer book* (5th ed.). Dublin, OH: Ahmadiyya Anjuman Isha'at-Islam.

American Psychiatric Association. (2013). *Diagnostic and statistical manual of mental disorders* (5th ed.). Arlington, VA: Author.

Anonymous (2015). *The Jewish prayer book* [Kindle version]. Retrieved from http://www.amazon.com

Bukkyō Dendō Kyōkai. (1995). *La ensenanza de Buda (The teaching of Buddha in Spanish and English)*. Moraga, CA: Society for the Promotion of Buddhism.

Campbell, T. C., & Campbell, T. M. (2016). *The China study: Revised and expanded*. New York, NY: Benbella Books.

Coue, E. (2006). *Self mastery through conscious autosuggestion*. Stilwell, KS: Digireads.com.

Dilts, R., & Halbom, T., & Smith, S. (2012). *Beliefs: Pathways to health and well-being* (2nd ed.). Bancyfelin, Wales: Crown House.

Erasmus, U. (1999). *Fats that heal, fats that kill*. Summertown, TN: Alive Books.

Gutman, J. (2008). *Glutathione: Your key to health*. Hudson, QC, Canada: Kudo.ca.

Murray-Wakelin, J. (2013). *Raw can cure cancer.* Melbourne, Australia: Brolga.

O'Keefe, T. (2013). *Inspiration for survive and prosper: Personal transformation out of crisis.* Fremantle, Australia: Australian Health and Education Centre.

Rossi, E. (1993). *The psychobiology of mind-body healing: New concepts of therapeutic hypnosis* (Rev. ed.). New York, NY: W. W. Norton.

Sarris, J., & Wardle, J. (2010). *Clinical naturopathy: An evidence-based guide to practice.* Sydney, Australia: Churchill Livingstone.

Schlosser, E. (2001). *Fast food nation: The dark side of the all-American meal.* London, England: Allen Lane.

US Catholic Church (1992). *Catechism of the Catholic Church.* Washington, D. C.: United States Conference of Catholic Bishops.

Vishnu-Devananda, S. (1999). *Meditation and mantras.* Delhi, India: Motilal Banarsidass.

Willey, D. (2014). *The Teachings of Confucius.* Salt Lake City, UT: Easy Publishing Company.

Afterword

It has been a pleasure to share with you what I do each week in my clinic helping people recover from addiction. While I am multidisciplinary, I am deeply dedicated to the practice of clinical hypnotherapy because of its power to change people's lives fast and help them recover from addiction quickly.

While I have made an exhaustive study of hypnosis, I advise you that knowledge alone does not hone the skills of the hypnotherapist. It is the combination of academic learning, observation and continuous practice that makes a good hypnotist and therapist. The confident hypnotherapist leads the client to where the client seeks to go and the addict towards living a clean and sober life.

For me as a clinical hypnotherapist and researcher, hypnotherapy is not something a clinician can tag on to their practice but a practice, science and discipline in and of itself. It demands considerable study and practice which, after great repetition, experimentation and supervision, can produce profound abilities for you to help clients stop addiction fast.

Start small with addictions. Only tackle opioids when you have a lot more experience as there is generally a higher level of co-pathology. Perhaps cross over from stopping smoking to including stopping cannabis to begin with. Do not be disheartened by any failures but take notes of where you need to improve treatment and refine your approach.

I advise fledgling therapists to work in the community as voluntary workers with drug and alcohol addiction projects. This helps you get used to working with addicts. It gives you a greater exposure to this clientele and the many problems they face on a day-to-day basis. The more comfortable you become working with addicts, the more you can focus on the techniques you use to help them recover from active addiction to live a clean and sober life.

Finally, I will re-emphasise to you, as I do with all students, the importance of regular clinical supervision with a supervisor who is used to working with drugs and alcohol. I do not consider peer supervision sufficient for working in the area of addiction. At the time of writing this, I have two supervisors and a coach, since I am in active clinical practice and teaching, who guide, challenge and provoke me to become better at what I do in the clinic.

Go forth and have the great pleasure of helping people become clean and sober.

Resources

I have made the following documents that I use in my clinic available for you to use as a guide to create your own. You can access them at the website URL provided below:

- Terms of therapy consultation form
- Client history-taking form
- Addiction questionnaire
- Addiction treatment contract
- Suicide questionnaire

Download these documents as PDFs and amend them for your own use from:

www.doctorok.com/addictionbookresources

Glossary

Within the text, you will find hypnotic and therapeutic phrases which you may need to extend your understanding of, so I have listed some below that you may find useful:

Active listening: Listening to the client and acknowledging their importance and the importance of their story. People need to feel that they have been heard and this is particularly the case for addicts, who often feel dismissed by others and society.

Alter-ego: A personality that is other than the main personality. Helping people create alter-ego personalities can sometimes help them overcome their perceived limitations. We all operate by our main and peripheral personalities, which, at times, interchange, each facilitating specific needs we may have.

Artificial somnambulism (referred to as somnambulism): An animated altered state of awareness when the client appears to be awake but is in some level of trance. They can communicate articulately and move around, yet they are not fully conscious.

'As if' frame: A psycho-imaginary scenario that tests a suggested reality. 'As if' frames are useful to help the client test out future possibilities inside their mind while being safe in the therapy room.

Association to self: Bringing the client into being aware of and comfortable with themselves. All addicts are dissociated from their bodies and personal agency. Recovery needs to bring them back to being in control of their bodies and self-directed choices.

Awareness perception: One of the most important concepts in Gestalt therapy is becoming aware of your world and reality. Many addicts have retreated from the outside world and are unaware of it and the way they live, so they are unable to negotiate life.

Awareness regulator: A series of thought patterns and mindsets that scan the external environment for perceived dangers or opportunities. In addiction recovery it is important for the therapist to help the client constantly scan their environment for the dangers of addiction.

Behavioural regulation suggestion: Asking the client to install mechanisms within their mind to regulate their behaviours. This includes installing Pavlovian responses as well as values within the superego. Healthy, happy, well-balanced people have the ability to regulate their behaviours, which is a skill that addicts need to learn.

Catalepsy: Physical immobility and non-responsiveness that occurs when a person enters into the trance state. The limbs may be waxy and flexible, so they can be placed into different positions and stay there, or they may be rigid and immovable. Also, with the correct suggestion, the body can be cataleptic but the person is still able to communicate with the hypnotist on cue. Catalepsy is also used for trance ratification.

Catatonia: The body is immobile and the person seems unresponsive to external stimuli. In hypnosis, a suggestion can be made for a catatonic state while the person specifically reacts to other suggestions.

Causal link: An implication that one thing is somehow related to another. It is a suggestion that when one thought, behaviour or emotion happens, another specified experience will follow.

Chemical dependency: When a person and others believe they cannot manage without any particular substance that causes an altered state awareness, other than homeostasis. The person and others may believe that the person cannot survive for even a few hours without that specific non-essential chemical, such as drugs or alcohol.

Chunking: Breaking experiences, concepts and processes into small units (chunking down) or assembling into larger units (chunking up). This can help mental processing become easier when the person is dealing with smaller units. It can also help the person build more complex thoughts, processes and behaviours from smaller units.

Clean and sober: Model of abstaining from all recreational drugs and alcohol and certain non-essential medications, including addictive and stimulating substances. The clean and sober model posits the person can never safely partake in these substances again in the future, as addiction may reoccur.

Cognitive monitoring: A person monitoring their own thoughts. It is the fundamental tenet of cognitive therapy.

Cognitive overload suggestion: Bombarding the client with multiple pieces of information to overload their mental processes, creating confusion, transderivational search, and rendering the person deeper into trance and more suggestible.

Cognitive shift: A change of mindset and thinking patterns. As therapists, we are always suggesting to and motivating the client to make constant unconscious and conscious changes. In addiction recovery, we are always motivating the client towards a clean and sober mindset.

Cognitive sorting suggestion: A suggestion to re-categorise memories, thought patterns and unconscious behavioural routines within the mind. As therapists, we are motivating the client to re-categorise the addictive behaviour as undesirable and the clean and sober way of living as desirable.

Command compliance: When a hypnotic subject complies to a suggestion, or a suggestion that was given to deepen an experience. Hypnotists need to continually test clients for command compliance during treatment as it may change due to extraneous and evolving events.

Compounding suggestion: A series of suggestions to deepen an experience. It is useful in hypnosis to move a client towards a cognitive, behavioural or emotional threshold, which causes change to happen.

Confabulation: The creation of alternative realties inside a person's mind and communication that is devoid of reality testing. These include lies and fantasies that have no basis in truth, deliberate deception or self-delusion, intentional or involuntary.

Conflict resolution: Getting the different parts of the mind to resolve their conflict with each other. One part of the mind can often be at odds with other parts, causing cognitive dissonance, which is always present during active addiction.

Contingent suggestion: A suggestion that delivers more than one suggestion in a phrase. It suggests that because one inevitable thought, behaviour, emotion, body function or event will happen, then so will another happen automatically.

Criteria of needs: The most important necessities of life. Addicts have lost sight of the high criteria of the need for health as they became consumed by addiction. In helping them become clean and sober, the therapist needs to help them to move the need for health up to become their highest priority.

Decontextualising: Suggesting that something be reframed into a different context. An idea or behaviour may seem worthy, yet when it is placed in a different context, a person can see that perhaps it is not productive. The reverse may be true.

Defence mechanism: A memory trace, mindset, behavioural

routine or behaviour that constantly or intermittently operates defensive thoughts and actions when encountering certain stimuli. We operate defence mechanisms to keep us safe; however, the addictive sub-personality can operate defensive behavioural sub-routines to defend the addiction. Hypnosis can help depotentiate those defence mechanisms to deliver new suggestions directly into the unconscious mind for living clean and sober and defending that way of living.

Direct suggestion: A commanding suggestion that the client will carry out the suggested action. Since resistance is lower during trance, people become more susceptible to act out direct suggestions.

Dissociation: The central core personality stepping to one side and a sub-personality taking control. It is a defensive mechanism that spontaneously happens at times of trauma. It may be induced purposefully to help a client gain a more global perspective.

Dissolving resistance: It is necessary at times for hypnotists to help the client dissolve any resistance they may have to following instructions, by dealing with their issues. The client may be unable to resolve the resistance consciously, so it is necessary to appeal to their unconscious mind to deliver compliance to hypnosis, suggestion and change.

Drivers: The values, beliefs and thoughts that drive our behaviours or experience. Addicts may only be partially aware of their drivers that operate their addiction. During recovery, they need to become fully aware of the drivers that motivate their clean and sober lifestyles in order to sustain recovery.

Drug dependency: When the person experiences a substance-induced altered state of awareness and begins to rely on that substance to maintain their believed sense of homeostasis. People tell themselves and others tell them that they are dependent on non-essential drugs, so they live the self-fulfilling prophecy of drug addiction.

Ego: Sigmund Freud's concept of the part of the structural model of the mind that regulates between the id and the superego. It can be easily damaged and is dysregulated during addiction. During addiction recovery, it is essential to strengthen the ego and reinstall its ability to control the demands of the id.

Ego Dystonic: When the behaviour, values and feelings (impulses, compulsions, desires and dreams) are not in line with the central goals of the ego. This disharmony disempowers the ego from carrying out its job of regulating between the id and the superego. In the case of the addict it is essential to restore harmony between the id, superego and ego in a way that allows the client to live clean and sober.

Ego-strengthening: Raising the client's self-esteem and self-worth. At every opportunity in addiction recovery, the therapist needs to continue to strengthen the client's ego by positive re-enforcement to restore it to its executive function.

Emotional driver: Suggesting certain emotions to motivate or change behaviour. Emotions, more so than thoughts, values, beliefs or behaviours drive change. The more intense the emotional experience, the faster the behavioural change.

Fact recall: Clients can recall past experiences. All memory recall is an estimated reconstruction. As a hypnotist, you can use elements of that recall positively to facilitate the client's change. It is important, however, for therapists not to treat that recall as accurate but simply representational. Some recall may be inaccurate or false memories.

Fight or flight response: When a person perceives that they are facing danger, they adopt a defensive mode of operation to either fight their way out of a situation or run away. All addicts are in a state of fight or flight, whether they consciously know that or not.

Fractionation: Taking something that the person experiences and feeding it back to them through suggestion in order to compound that experience. It can be used in trance deepening or to help someone experience something more intensely.

Future pacing: Placing the client's mindset into their future, by suggestion, as they carry out thoughts, actions, behaviours and emotions related to that suggested future. It is used in trial therapy, desensitisation and rehearsal therapy.

Goal-directed behaviour: Focused behaviour that aims to take the person specifically towards one or more goals. Addicts need help in formulating, clarifying and implementing their goals around living clean and sober.

Grammatically incorrect hidden suggestion: The use of incongruent grammar to cause confusion and deliver a hidden suggestion. Incorrect grammar is frequently difficult for the conscious mind to process, forcing the person to use unconscious processing. When the incorrect grammar produces incomprehensible communications, the unconscious mind has to pay more attention to what is said and often accepts hidden suggestions.

Higher self: The ideal self. Since addicts have such damaged egos, they no longer have a vision of their ideal selves. The ideal self of being clean and sober is not only desirable but also aspirational and may even have a spiritual element. As therapists we need to act as facilitators to help the client move towards their higher self and acknowledging when they have achieved that goal.

Hypersensitivity suggestion: A suggestion that increases the experience of one or more sensory experiences, either through external sensory perception or within our own imagination. Suggesting greater sensitivity around ordinary, everyday, pleasurable experiences reconnects the addict with the joys of living without the substance of abuse.

Hyper-vigilance suggestion: A suggestion to be hyper-aware of external stimuli or increase sensitivity to external stimuli. In addiction recovery, it is necessary to motivate the client to be highly vigilant of their environment and the people around them so they do not once again become embroiled in addictive behaviours.

Hypno-analysis: The examining of the unconscious memories via hypnotic suggestion. The exploration of those memories may be carried out during hypnosis and blocked from consciousness via suggestion or amnesia. Suggestion can also be given to make those memories available to the conscious mind.

Hypnotic repetition: A recurring suggestion. It may be the repetition of the same suggestion or the delivery of that suggestion in many different forms, formats or configuration. It is suggestion bombardment which works on the principle that familiarity creates comfort and acceptance.

Id: Sigmund Freud's concept of the instinctual primitive part of the mind that seeks pleasure such as food, sex, or intoxication. The id has no rational abilities. It is like the hungry child that wants what it wants and must be regulated by the values within the superego. Out of control, the id becomes destructive.

Illusion of choice suggestion: A suggestion that seems to give options (transformational grammar surface language) but has been framed by other suggestions to give the client only one choice (deep root language). So the client is led by illusion to the inevitable choice the therapist has suggested.

Implied directive: To suggest that something will happen using indirect language and suggestion. It is subtle implication within the communication and a form of indirect suggestion. It may even be hidden within a metaphor.

Indirect suggestion: A suggestion casually hidden in a communication that implies the likelihood of a thought or action taking place. It may even be placed in a metaphor. It is a linguistic modal operator of possibility, or even probability, but not necessity.

Interrogative deepener: A question used to force the client to go inside into the unconscious mind, deeper into trance, to find the answer to a question or puzzle. The question or puzzle is too complex or unsuitable for the conscious mind to process.

Interrogative suggestion: A suggestion phrased as a question. There may even be verbal marking in the question that hides a direct or indirect suggestion. The question is phrased in order to lead the client to an inevitable outcome. Since there is no direct suggestion, it avoids resistance and is a form of backward communication.

Intra-hypnotic suggestion: A suggestion that commands the hypnotic subject to comply with a suggestion while in the trance state. It demands instant action in the present time by using present-tense language or suggestion for a real-time experience.

Kinaesthetic control: Suggestion that the person has control over their physical bodily functions and experiences. It creates the illusion they are in control, boosts their ego and prepares them to be receptive to further suggestions. What it also does is train the hypnotic subject how to control their body when they need to in a way that the addict has forgotten or never knew how to do.

Locking the gate: Using a yes-set followed by a no-set to confirm the compliance to a suggestion. Hypnotists must check their work as therapy progresses to see if the client has accepted suggestions and made the requested changes. With addiction, it is useful for the hypnotist to continually use locking the gate, as addicts habitually confabulate. Locking the gate can also be when a communication is phrased to direct the client in one direction only, with no return to dysfunctional behaviour.

Memory recall: Remembering a previous thought, behaviour, emotion or experience; and a form of regression. It is important to remember that all memories obtained under hypnosis are only a representation of the past. Therapists should respect the person's experience, yet remain objective.

Metaphor: A story or example that carries a message and indirect suggestion for change. Metaphor as a form of indirect suggestion is a story with which the clients can associate, so they become emotionally attached to the central characters. With addicts it is important to give them examples of people in similar situations as themselves who have overcome their difficulties and gone on to lead happy, strong, clean and sober lives.

Modalities: The five senses of sight (visual (V), sound (auditory (A), feeling (kinaesthetic (K), taste (gustatory (G) and smell (olfactory (O). The experiences can be a result of external (e) sensory awareness or internal (i) imagination. They may have a positive association for the person (+) or be a negative (-) and unpleasant experience. So, for example, a positive imaginary feeling would be (Ki+), etc.

Modelling suggestion: A suggestion to emulate someone else or a version of the earlier, ideal self or imagined self. From when we are young children we learn to model parts of other people's behaviour, some good, some not good. In addiction recovery, we need to get the clients to model clean and sober behaviours.

Negative hallucination: Sensory deletion of a real experience, due to the suggestion that the person's mind edits sensory input. For example, hypnotically suggested blindness or deafness. As hypnotists, we can also suggest that people have negative hallucinations for the past perceived positive experience of substance abuse.

No-set: Creating an agreement, compliance or series of actions with the client, through suggestion, such as (ideo-motor responses) head shakes from side to side, which puts the client into a mindset of agreeing to say 'no' to a question.

Pacing: Matching the person's experience to create empathy and therapeutic alliance. You may match body language, breathing or language patterns. While pacing creates empathy, consciously or unconsciously, it needs to be a doorway to lead the client to making the changes in the thoughts, behaviours and emotions that need to take place.

Parts negotiation: Hypnotically eliciting different sub-personalities and drivers within the unconscious mind and getting them to talk to each other in order to resolve conflict. Addicts are always in conflict, particularly when they present for treatment. You can ask the client to let the different parts within them come to an agreement that will take them forward to becoming clean and sober. This can also be done by creating psychodynamic conflict with the client, forcing them to move towards resolution of conflict.

Pattern disruption: The disruption of thoughts, behaviours or emotions. Addicts repeat the same automatic addictive behaviour patterns day after day. Treatment needs to be focused on disrupting those patterns and installing new, healthier patterns.

Pattern interrupter: A suggestion or behavioural intervention that initiates the disruption of thoughts and behaviours. Pattern interrupters are used to create pattern disruption. During addiction recovery treatment, therapists may use many pattern interrupter strategies to get the client to change their behaviours.

Pavlovian response: A programmed and installed response to a certain stimulus. This response can be brought about by suggestion or repeated exposure to certain stimuli associated with a particular response. Repetition builds the strength of that response.

Permissive suggestion: Using indirect language and modal operators of possibility to make a suggestion for an action. Permissive suggestion is more subtle than direct suggestion and is used to bypass resistance to change.

Phonological ambiguity: A word or phrase that sounds like another word or phrase and delivers two or more suggestions. It is a double entendre meant to deliver two or more communications. It can also create confusion and transderivational search.

Physical reintegration: When the person's dissociated personality becomes central stage once again and they become aware of the physical body. Addicts are dissociated from their bodies via the simple fact they are in an altered state of awareness. Becoming clean and sober requires the addict to once again become integrated and attentive to their physical body.

Positive emotional drivers: Installing in the client, via suggestion or setting up psychodynamic change, good internal feelings (Ki+) that drive thoughts, values, beliefs, emotions and behaviours. The hypnotist needs to continually install positive emotional drivers to create change.

Positive hallucination: The creation of an internal psycho-imaginary experience, through suggestion, that the person hallucinates something that is not there. Creating positive hallucinations that guide the client towards what a good life it is to be clean and sober can help motivate them.

Post-hypnotic suggestion: A suggestion that the subject carries out a thought, behaviour, action or emotion when they come out of the official trance state. A specific time frame or frequency can even be suggested. Repetition of that response can also be suggested.

Pre-hypnosis: Actions taken by the hypnotist before hypnosis to prepare the subject for hypnotisability and suggestibility. Pre-hypnosis can also be a series of processes used to test the client's responsiveness.

Pre-supposition: A communication that assumes that something else is automatically true. These are used in loading communications to motivate psychological change. Since it is a complex communication, the conscious mind has less time to offer resistance.

Psycho-imaginary visualisation: Constructing scenarios and alternative realities inside the mind. While visualisations are related to sight, they may also ignite auditory, kinaesthetic and other sensory internal experiences. Such visualisations may also motivate perceived external sensory experiences and motivate behaviour.

Ratification: Ratifying is testing what the client is experiencing in a trance-like state and their reactions to suggestions. It is important hypnotically to get clients to ratify trances so it increases their confidence in hypnosis.

Reality testing: Being aware what is true, what is not true, and orientation in the world. Addicts have poor reality testing and part of recovery needs to be to teach them to have good reality testing so they can stay clean and sober.

Reintegration: The process of melding back together fractured sub-personalities. Also, the repositioning of the dissociated core personality back into its central operational role. The central core, self-caring personality that promotes homeostasis is deposed during active addiction and must be reinstated.

Repeating suggestion: A suggestion that will continue to repeat inside the client's mind.

Resistance: When a client is not accepting certain suggestions. You can allow the client to gather resistance and then let it go via suggestion.

Safety anchor: A programmed cue/response mechanism in any of the five senses that may be triggered at times when the client feels unsafe or goes into an abreaction, to bring them back to a sense of safety.

Secondary gain: These are benefits that arise from having a dysfunctional behaviour. A person experiences benefits from being an addict, such as social security payments, special compensation for their poor behaviours or sympathy from others.

Self-agency: Being in control of your thoughts, actions and behaviours. People who have a sense that they are not in control of their lives have no sense of self-agency. The non-active addict must experience self-agency that supports them staying clean and sober.

Self-efficacy: The belief you are in control of your thoughts, actions and behaviours. Self-efficacy can also include an overall set of beliefs in your own capabilities. When working with an addict, the therapist must help them get from a place of 'I can't do this' to 'I can live my life clean and sober every day'.

Sensory deprivation suggestion: The suggestion that someone loses touch with their external senses, which makes them more suggestible because the suggestion is accepted without competition. In using hypnosis, the hypnotist must be clear with the client that the hypnotist's voice can still deliver suggestion.

Situational suggestion: A suggestion that something specific will happen in certain situations. This may be locational or a time-related situation, one that involved meeting certain people or finding yourself in certain situations wherever you might be in your life.

Solution-focused therapy: Therapy that moves the client constantly to solutions and does not allow them to remain in the problem state. While working with addicts, therapists need to use many techniques, including regression. The overall direction of recovery therapy needs to be taking the client towards being clean and sober, fast.

Somnambulism: An animated altered state of awareness when the client appears to be awake but is in some level of trance or asleep. Sleep walking is regarded as naturally occurring somnambulism. Some people are natural somnambulists and have a high level of ability to be in different levels of consciousness at the same time.

State-changing suggestion: A suggestion for fast change of the physical, mental and emotional state. This requires direct command suggestion and has been used in India for many years in different kinds of yoga practices. Addicts need to practise state-changing so they can recover from panic states.

State recall suggestion: A suggestion to recall and re-experience a previously experienced state, so recalling a state-dependent experience. This is a form of experiential regression. We all have memory traces of our experiences which we naturally recall instantly but can also be taught to recall voluntarily.

Straight edge: A cultural movement, which started in the punk era, of like-minded people who do not take recreational drugs, drink alcohol or engage in sex with multiple partners. For some people who feel they do not fit into societal mainstream, straight edge is a way for them to identify with a clean and sober cultural group.

Suggestion for multiple time use: A suggestion that can operate in the person's perception of the past, present or future. It is used to cause cognitive and emotional shifts around experience in the different time zones all at the same time.

Suggestion loop: A recurring, repetitious suggestion that carries on, continually going around and around inside the person's mind. The suggestion needs to install a repeater action inside the person's mind for the message the communication carries.

Suggestion response training: Giving people easy suggestions to follow so they establish a tendency to follow suggestions. It is possible to train people to follow suggestions by repeatedly giving them suggestions that produce rewards for them.

Superego: Sigmund Freud's concept of the part of the mind that contains our values, morals, ideals and codes by which we live. In addicts, the superego is unable to do its job of keeping the person safe. The therapist needs to encourage and model values, morals and ideals in the client's superego that promote living and remaining clean and sober.

Therapeutic alliance: A co-operative process of the therapist and the client working together.

Time disorientation: Suggestion for taking the hypnotic subject out of a sense of ordinary, wakeful, linear time. It can be used to help a client go into trance.

Time distortion: A suggestion to experience external clock time differently from internal subjective time.

Time framing: Suggesting the client is experiencing something within a particular time frame, for example, the past, present or future.

Time scanning: The client looking at experiences across time frames.

Time shift: Shifting the person's attention to another time frame.

Trance deepener: A suggestion of an action that sends the client deep into the self-absorbed trance state.

Transderivational search: When the conscious mind is overloaded by too much information or a problem it cannot solve, the person goes inside to the unconscious mind in order to make sense of the situation. It is a way of inducing or deepening trance by depotentiating conscious awareness. Suggestibility is increased. Also used to disengage the critical mechanisms that reside in the conscious mind which often interfere with the effectiveness of suggestions.

Truism: A statement that is clearly true. It can be used before a suggestion to prepare the subject for acceptance of the suggestion.

If someone believes that something is true, it increases the efficacy of the ensuing suggestion.

Unconscious resolution: Suggestion that the unconscious mind solves a problem all on its own and lets the conscious mind know when that has happened. The therapist ushers this along by direct or indirect suggestion.

Word salad: A jumble of words designed to cause confusion, forcing the client into trance. They may be grammatically incorrect or have no grammatical structure at all. The conscious mind grapples for logic and when it cannot find it, it searches within the unconscious, therefore rendering the person into trance.

Yes-set: Creating an agreement, compliance or series of actions, such as head nods, which puts the client into a mindset of agreeing to suggestions as a matter of habit. This can include ideo motor responses or the client simply agreeing by giving 'yes' answers to questions.

Printed by Amazon Italia Logistica S.r.l.
Torrazza Piemonte (TO), Italy